+15 −

Science

503266

The Newcomen Society for the Study of the History of Engineering and Technology

Extra Publication No. 6

SAMUEL MORLAND, age 33, from the painting by Sir Peter Lely
in the possession of the Carolina Art Association

Sir Samuel Morland

DIPLOMAT AND INVENTOR

1625-1695

BY

H. W. DICKINSON
D.Eng.(Hon.), M.I.Mech.E.

PUBLISHED FOR
THE NEWCOMEN SOCIETY
BY W. HEFFER AND SONS LIMITED
CAMBRIDGE
1970

ISBN 0 85270 061 X

Printed in Great Britain by W. Heffer and Sons Ltd, Cambridge

CONTENTS

ILLUSTRATIONS

ACKNOWLEDGEMENTS

The Frontispiece is reproduced by the Courtesy of the Carolina Art Association, Gibbes Art Gallery, Charleston, South Carolina, U.S.A. Plates I and VI are reproduced by permission of the Director of the Science Museum, London; Crown Copyright reserved. Plates VIII, IX and Figs. 1 and 2 are reproduced by permission of the Trustees of the British Museum, London. Plate V is reproduced by permission of the Librarian, Trinity College, Cambridge. Plates IV and VII are reproduced by permission of the Director, Istituto e Museo di Storia Della Scienza, Florence. Plate XII is reproduced by permission of the Director of the Victoria and Albert Museum, London.

EDITORS' PREFACE

The late Dr. Henry Winram Dickinson was born at Ulverston, Lancashire, on 28 August 1870. In the course of a distinguished career at the Science Museum, South Kensington, he became Keeper of Mechanical Engineering and so had charge of steam engines and pumping machinery. No doubt the early history of these subjects aroused his interest in Sir Samuel Morland as inventor both of the packed plunger pump and, though less certainly, of a high pressure steam engine.

The Council of the Newcomen Society decided to publish this biography of Morland in 1970 to mark the 50th anniversary of the Society's foundation and as a further tribute to the memory of Dr. Dickinson in the centennial year of his birth. As a Founder and as Honorary Secretary for over thirty years, his services to the Newcomen Society would alone have been invaluable, but in addition he edited single-handed the first twenty-five volumes of the Transactions.

The wide range of subjects in engineering history on which Dr. Dickinson (President 1932–34) was a leading authority is shown by the extensive list of his writings, which is published here for the first time as Appendix IV.

The value of this Golden Jubilee Memorial Volume is two-fold; it describes Morland's inventions, some of which were ahead of their time; it also throws more light on the life of a public servant in England and abroad during the period of the Commonwealth under Cromwell, and it gives

Morland's own account of how he thwarted the plot to assassinate King Charles II just before his Restoration in 1660.

In August 1942 Rhys Jenkins, aged 83, wrote to Dr. Dickinson: 'I have had Morland in mind for more than 20 years and am still unable to define his character except to say that he had no sense of the value of money. He has been called a double spy but that, I think, is a misconception.' Dr. Dickinson suggested the book should be published as their combined work but Rhys Jenkins wrote in November: 'I have read your Morland manuscript; you must cut out my name. When I asked if you would take up the subject, it was without the least idea of joint authorship—in fact it would be very difficult to get any two men who would come to the same conclusions on the evidence available.' Rhys Jenkins died in 1953, aged 93.

Dr. Dickinson had intended to enter his manuscript on Morland in a biographical contest organized by Hamish Hamilton Ltd, but he died on 21 February 1952, a month before the closing date, and the manuscript and illustrations were not ready. The late Miss G. Bingham O.B.E. (Assistant Secretary of the Newcomen Society 1939–54) who died in February 1964, wrote in 1952: 'When Dr. Dickinson was very ill last January, he sent me the manuscript of his Morland book, asking if I would type it for him. Although I do not do these long typing jobs now, I was only too pleased to do it for him for love.'

The Editors wish to record gratefully the help given by the late Professor Henry Douglas Dickinson M.A., the author's son, formerly of Leeds and Bristol Universities, who preserved the original manuscript and made useful amendments; both he and the late L. E. Harris (President 1957–59) also provided illustrations. The Editors sincerely thank the Librarian of the Royal Society; also Mr. K. R.

Gilbert M.A. (Vice-President) for drawing their attention to Morland's calculating machines in Florence and to the miniature of Morland in the Victoria and Albert Museum; and they especially appreciate the guidance given to them by Dr. Stanley B. Hamilton O.B.E. (President 1944–46 and Editor of the Transactions since 1952) in the production of this Golden Jubilee Memorial Volume.

ARTHUR STOWERS
RODNEY J. LAW

AUTHOR'S PREFACE

It is a truism that the roots of the present are to be found in the past and the momentous economic and social changes, commonly called the Industrial Revolution, which is portrayed as having commenced in England in the middle of the 18th century, are now realized to have begun in the previous century or even earlier. The national policy of the Tudor sovereigns was to encourage the establishment of industries and improvements in the arts; the results were beginning to appear in the 17th century. This was the century of great political changes in England which have obscured other developments. Acute minds, however, were directing their attention to science and technology; too little notice has been taken of their labours in view of their importance to their successors. Such a 'labourer in the vineyard' was Sir Samuel Morland, Baronet, 'Master of Mechanicks' to His Majesty King Charles II.

It seemed to the author and his friend, Rhys Jenkins, that the life of a man like Sir Samuel Morland, concerned as he was in the political events of the Commonwealth period and accountable for distinct steps in technical progress, was worth telling as being of interest to historians and to technical readers.

Four phases in Morland's career stand out pre-eminently: (1) his academic upbringing, (2) his incursion into politics, (3) his outburst of invention and (4) his refuge in the consolations of religion in his old age. In the first phase he attained a profundity of learning beyond that of a university man of his day, fitting him for high employment. In the second, he entered the political arena and became the servant of Cromwell, who gave him high office because of his academic attainments.

After Cromwell's death, he went over to the Royalist side and aided the Restoration of King Charles II. In the scramble for preferment he found himself ignored and so turned to the third phase, that of cultivating inventions and devices, hoping thereby to gain the King's patronage. In this he succeeded, which led to his being accredited to the Court of Louis XIV as the outstanding English engineer of his time. But this did not bring the fame for which he had hoped, and for the rest of his life he was a disappointed man.

The conception of this biography took place before the first World War and was due to the inspiration of my colleague Rhys Jenkins (President 1923–25), formerly of H.M. Patent Office. On my undertaking the task, he generously placed at my disposal a vast amount of material which he had collected during twenty years, and this has been supplemented by my own research, which was interrupted by the second World War. Reduction and research having now been carried as far as practicable, this work is offered to the indulgence of the reader.

Generous help has been received from many sources. Thanks are due to the authorities at Winchester College; Magdalene College, Trinity College and the University Library, Cambridge; Lambeth Palace Library; the Public Record Office, the British Museum, the Science Museum South Kensington; and to numerous friends.

H. W. DICKINSON

Purley, Surrey, 1952

CONSPECTUS VITAE

1664   Project for opening correspondence

1666   Made arithmetical machine

1666   Designed circular cipher

1668   Appointed Secretary to the Commissioners for
        Ireland

1669   Appointed Commissioner of Appeal in Excise

1670   Married Carola, daughter of Sir Roger Harsnett

1671   Invented speaking trumpet

1672   Published translation of book on fortifications

1673   Warrant to erect printing press

1673   Published description of arithmetical instrument

1674   Petition and patent for engine for raising water

1674   Showed pump at Grocers' Hall

1674   Improved ships' capstan

1675   Forced water to the top of the tower at Windsor

1675   Isaac Thompson advertised price list of his pumps

1675   Leased Vauxhall House for 31 years

1676   Married Anne, daughter of George Filding of
        Solihull

1677   Designed Inclined Tube Barometer

1681   Demonstration of pumps before the King at
        Windsor

1681   Created 'Master of Mechanicks'

1681 Married daughter of Frost, a lawyer

1681 Accredited to Louis XIV as Consultant for water supply of Versailles

1681 John Evelyn visited him at Vauxhall

1682 Requested Dr. Pell for arithmetical tables

1682 High pressure steam engine

1684 Removed to a house at Hammersmith

1685 Death of his patron, Charles II

1686 Designed gun carriage

1687 Unfortunate fifth marriage and divorce

1688 Abdication of James II

1688 Suggested to Thomas Tenison an edition of Euclid's *Elements*

1689 Wrote his Autobiography

1690 Examiner of building at Hampton Court

1692 Went blind

1695 Presented well to Hammersmith

1695 Archbishop Tenison and John Evelyn visited him at Hammersmith

1695 Death at Hammersmith

CHAPTER I

EARLY DAYS
1625–53

Family; Birth; Upbringing; Academic life; Commonwealth;
Sides with Cromwell

Samuel Morland was one of several children of the Rev. Thomas Morland, M.A., of Queen's College, Oxford, who is believed to have come originally from Westmorland. He may have been a scion of the Morland family of Copplethwaite and Killing Halls, Westmorland. There were several Morland families in the Kirkby Stephen district in the 17th cent. as evidenced by the Hearth Tax Rolls.[1] Thomas Morland was Rector of Sulhampstead Banister, 6½ m. S.S.W. of Reading Berkshire, from 1625 till his death in 1650. From 1615 till 1625 he is believed to have been Rector of Brightonwalton, 9½ m. N. of Newbury in the same county; the truth of this or otherwise we have not succeeded in establishing. It is a foregone assumption that the father, in view of the oath of supremacy that he must have taken and from the fact that he was a priest of the Church of England, was of the Royalist persuasion. The dates and even the place of birth of Samuel and of his brothers, Thomas and Martin, are not certainly known; in neither of the baptismal Registers of the parishes mentioned is there any record of their baptisms. The year of Samuel's

---

[1] There is a village of Morland 7 m. S.E. of Penrith and 3 m. S. of the former railway station of Cliburn, Cumberland.

birth is usually given as 1625, this being based on the statement of his little book, *The Urim of Conscience*, 1695, to be
noticed subsequently, that he was then 'already past the
Seventieth Year of his age.' This is, however, the loose kind
of statement that a person commonly makes; assuming that
the words were penned in the year of publication and not
earlier, this could mean that he was born in 1624 or 1625; as
we shall see later, the latter is the more likely date.

The year 1625 was an important one, for it was that in
which Charles I succeeded to the throne. In the years following, although the father may have had his misgivings about
the conduct of the King and his attempts to govern uncon-
stitutionally, yet we can only assume that the children were
brought up with the Royalist outlook and that their early
education was cared for by their father.

We have no record of any incident that occurred in
Samuel's boyhood, spent doubtless at Sulhampstead, a
place as much removed from the busy haunts of men as
could well be found. Yet Berkshire, where the village is
situated, is one of the Home Counties which were particularly involved in the struggle between the King and Parliament, and some repercussions of it must have been felt there.
Newbury, only 12 miles away was the scene of two hard-
fought battles between Charles and the Earl of Essex, on
20 September 1643, and between the King and the Earl of
Manchester, on 27 October 1644. Before this time, however, Samuel had started on his education.

He was admitted to Winchester College[2] in 1639, his age,
that of the time of his election and presumably that of his
admission, being given as twelve; that would make the year
of his birth 1626; perhaps he was in his thirteenth year. Here
he spent five years, living under the austerity of that foundation on the frugal fare then provided and progressing in

[2] Kirby, T. F., *Winchester Scholars*, 1888, p. 178.

literae humaniores, the only studies then pursued in any of our public schools.

From the School he went on to the University and entered Magdalene College, Cambridge. In the Admission Book, 1644, his entry is thus recorded: 'Samuel Moreland, son of Thomas Moreland, Priest, was admitted Sizar in the College —May in the 19th year of his age; a boy of Wickham's College near Winchester. Tutor Sir Turner.' This would make the date of his birth 1625. Nineteen was rather late if anything, at that period, for a boy to enter the University; the age then was more usually sixteen, but there may have been financial difficulties or possibly delays due to the Civil War that was rending the country. There is a similar obscurity about the dates of birth of two of the brothers of Samuel whose existence is known. Thomas, an elder brother, matriculated at Queen's College, Oxford, 9 November 1632, at the age of 16. Another brother, Martin, entered Winchester College, his age in 1636 being given as eleven; he proceeded to Wadham College, Oxford, where he matriculated 16 June 1644, his age then being given as twenty.[3] There is such a wide discrepancy here that it may be possible that Samuel and Martin were children of a second marriage and that financial difficulties had delayed their proceeding to the Universities.

To return to Samuel's career, there is, in the British Museum,[4] a small bound volume, lettered on the spine 'Sir S. Morland's Accompt Book at Cambridge, 1644'; there is no internal evidence that it belonged to him, but in any case the title could not be contemporary because of the use of the designation 'Sir'. We accept the volume at its face

[3] Martin Morland was inducted into the living of Weld (? Wield, 5½ m. W. of Alton, Co. Hants.), but was ejected at the Restoration because he refused to take the oath of supremacy to Charles II. Particulars of this branch of the Morland family are given in *Notes and Queries*, 12 Ser. 143 and 313.

[4] Sloane MS. 138.

value; there are two entries that are significant: 'I came to Magdalene Coll. May the 22 1644. I came from London Aprill 25. I entered into Commons Aprill the 28.' The other entry is 'I came from London the 9 of August I enter'd Commons August the 16.'

Now ensued a settled academic career, not differing in character and duration from that of hundreds of alumni of his time and since. What the curriculum was like may be judged from a letter written in 1646 by Henry Power,[5] a graduate of Cambridge, who was apparently studying medicine: 'My years in the University are whole up to a midle bachelaur-shippe which height of a graduate I am sure ought to speake him indefective in any part of philosophy. Our second yeare of sophistry is always taken up in physicall contemplation.'

Morland's learning must have been wide and also deep, if we judge from his subsequent literary output. The spoken and written academic tongue was Latin and it is evident that he had studied Greek and Hebrew; also French necessarily, as it was the language of polite intercourse and of diplomacy. He took his B.A. degree in 1648, and his M.A. in 1652; on 30 November 1649 he was elected a Fellow of his College, becoming a Tutor in the following year. He retained his Fellowship till 1653, his last signature in the College books being of that date. It is of interest to note that he figured in the capacity of Tutor on the occasion of the entry of the subsequently famous Samuel Pepys into the College in October 1650 and signed his admission form. This acquaintance ripened into friendship in later years, as we shall learn later.

At the stage of a University man's career now reached by Morland, the easiest course, as it was the usual one, was to take Holy Orders and accept a College or other living;

[5] Halliwell, J. O., *Letters on Scientific Subjects*, 1841, p. 91.

indeed, family tradition pointed in that direction. But no! This is what he tells us actually happened: 'Having received my education in Winchester Colledg, I was removed to the University of Cambridg. Where haveing spent 9 or 10 years, I was sollicited by some freinds to take upon mee the Ministry, for which, fearing I was not fitly qualified, I betook myself to ye study of ye Mathematicks.'[6]

This is what could be expected. Englishmen who grew to manhood during the time of the Civil Wars realised little of the tyranny which gave zeal and fire to the religion of their fathers. During this period at Cambridge the atmosphere, unlike that at Oxford, was strongly in favour of the Parliament and against the King. Morland found himself amid a ferment of new ideas; he encountered a spirit of scepticism, of doubt and of free enquiry. His horizon widened and his political outlook, though Royalist to begin with, underwent a gradual change. For his decision on conscientious grounds not to enter Holy Orders, he deserves much credit. It may be he was sufficiently vain to believe that his talents were such that they would be wasted in a country parsonage. He would be influenced too in his decision by the prospect of a more active life than that afforded by an academic or pastoral career. It was reasonable to suppose that the existing regime had come to stay and that it would be advisable to swim with the stream. That he embraced some of the principles of the Parliamentary party has been definitely stated. A decisive change thus took place in Morland's life and to his subsequent career we must now turn.

[6] Lambeth Palace Library MS. 931. This is the *Abbreviat* of his life or autobiography by Morland himself and as such is deserving of every credence. We shall quote from it repeatedly under the title *Autobiography*. It is quoted in full by Halliwell *loc. cit.*, p. 116, and is reproduced in this volume in Appendix III.

CHAPTER II

THE CAREER OPENS TO
THE TALENTS
1653–61

Accompanies Whitelocke's Embassy to Sweden; Sent by Cromwell to relieve the Waldenses; Clerk of the Signet; First Marriage; Reveals plot to assassinate Charles II; Death of Cromwell; Goes over to the Royalist side

Having decided against taking Holy Orders and feeling within him the ability to occupy a wider field than that offered by University life, anxious also to find some opening, Morland seized upon an opportunity to accompany Bulstrode Whitelocke, (1605–75), appointed Ambassador to Queen Christina of Sweden, in order to arrange a treaty of amity and commerce between the two countries, a step in Cromwell's policy of enlarging English influence on the Continent. How this opportunity came to Morland we do not know. At this juncture John Thurloe, (1616–68), was Secretary of the Council of State under Cromwell, and may have heard of Morland. It is probable that Thurloe had some connection already with the University of Cambridge, because he became Member of Parliament for that constituency in 1659. By taking this opportunity it can be said that Morland cast in his lot definitely with the Parliamentary Party. He was one of the suite of Whitelocke's Embassy, about a hundred persons in number, and occupied the not inconsiderable position of one of the 'Gentlemen admitted to Whitelocke's table.' One can only suppose that he was chosen because of his academic status and his knowledge of Latin and French, the two languages used in diplomacy. We can imagine the stir that must have been occasioned in the preparation of the outfit needed for such a journey.

Whitelocke's party left London eventually on 2 November 1653, embarked at Gravesend on the 5th and arrived at Gothenburg[7] on the 15th. Queen Christina was the daughter of the great Gustavus Adolphus (1611–32) and, on his death, succeeded to the throne when only six years of age. She proved herself a great patron of scientific men, of whom we may mention Salmasius, Grotius, and Descartes. Thus the atmosphere into which Morland was introduced was highly stimulating. It can hardly be considered that this Embassy was a desirable introduction for Morland to public life. Despite the restraining Puritan influence of Whitelocke, and it was not inconsiderable, life in Uppsala must have led to habits of extravagance and idleness, if not of dissipation. All that we can learn of Morland's duties and employment during this time is that on one occasion, Queen Christina desiring to learn English, M. de la Marche, one of the Chaplains of the Embassy, drew up a grammar which 'was fairly written in English and French by Mr. Moreland'.[8] During the long winter that the Embassy spent in Sweden it is recorded[9] that 'they had disputations in Latin among the young men who were scholars,' of whom Morland must have been a leader, for he would now be about twenty-eight years of age.

During the time the Embassy was in Sweden important events took place: at home, Oliver Cromwell assumed the

---

[7] Whitelocke, B., *Journal of the Swedish Embassy*, new ed. 1855, Vol. I, p. 77.
[8] *Ibid.*, p. 394.
[9] *Ibid.*, Vol. II, p. 354.

supreme authority as Lord Protector of the Commonwealth; in Sweden, Queen Christina announced her intention of resigning the Crown to her cousin, who thus became Charles X.

The Treaty with Sweden was concluded satisfactorily on 11 April 1654; on the return journey the party travelled to Hamburg, arriving 10 June, and embarked at Glückstadt on the 17th. The vessel experienced a very stormy voyage, eventually being cast ashore on the Norfolk coast near Yarmouth on 28 June, fortunately without mishap. Whitelocke received the thanks of Parliament for his success on this mission.

We conclude that Morland conducted himself satisfactorily at the Embassy, judging from Whitelocke's report about him which stated that he was 'a very civil man and an excellent scholar; modest and respectful; perfect in the Latin tongue; an ingenious mechanist.' With such an excellent character, it is not surprising that Morland was able to secure further official employment. Morland's own account is as follows: 'At my return I was recommended to Secretary Thurlo for an assistant and in a few months time after, sent by Cromwell as an envoy to the Duke of Savoy in behalf of the Protestants of the Valleys of Piedmont.'[10]

What Morland's duties were exactly we are not informed, but the qualifications for being chosen as 'Commissioner Extraordinary', for such was his rank, to the Duke of Savoy were doubtless the attainments that had led to his inclusion in the Embassy to Sweden, coupled with the ability he had shown then and subsequently. Needless to say, it was for Morland an important event; for Cromwell it was a further opportunity to make a stand abroad as protector of the reformed religion—the first interference in foreign affairs made without interested motives in our history, an inter-

[10] *Autobiography*, Appendix III.

ference that has been followed in similar cases to our credit during succeeding centuries to the present day.

The inhabitants of the valleys of Piedmont had embraced the reformed religion under the teaching of Peter Waldo and were consequently known as Waldenses, otherwise as Vaudois. The Duke of Savoy, their ruler, had issued an edict forbidding the Waldenses to practice their religion and had commenced on 7 April 1655 a persecution of much barbarity. The news of their sufferings excited the sympathy of fellow Protestants in this country and in Switzerland. Cromwell ordered a collection of money in the parishes throughout England in aid of the sufferers. The opinion of the day is reflected in Milton's Sonnet XIII—'On the late Massacre in Piedmont.'

> AVENGE O Lord, thy slaughter'd saints whose bones
>   Lie scattered on the Alpine mountains cold;
> Even them who kept thy truth so pure of old,
>   When all our fathers worshipp'd stocks and stones
> Forget not: in thy book record their groans
>   Who were thy sheep, and in their ancient fold
> Slain by the bloody Piedmontese that roll'd
>   Mother with infant down the rocks; their moans
> The vales redoubled to the hills; and they
>   To heaven. Their martyr'd blood and ashes sow
>   O'er all the Italian fields, where still doth sway
> The triple tyrant; that from these may grow
>   A hundred fold, who having learn'd the way
>   Early may flee the Babylonian woe.

Morland's duty, besides expostulating with the Duke, was to obtain if possible a recall of the edict; he was charged also with dispensing on the spot the alms that had been collected in England. In this and in other matters he acted under our Ambassador to Switzerland, Dr. John Pell,

(1616–85) known as a mathematician, whose headquarters were in Geneva; he was Ambassador there from 1654 till 1658.

The correspondence between Thurloe, Pell and Morland is detailed by Vaughan[11] and from it we cull the salient facts: Morland left England on 23 May 1655 and was with the French Court at La Ferté on the 26th, where he tried to induce Louis XIV to interfere in order to stop the persecution. It was surprising that Cromwell should have thought this visit worth while, for His Most Catholic Majesty was then only seventeen years of age. Perhaps Cromwell banked on the good feeling of the youthful King; however, Cardinal Mazarin held the reins of government. Morland, at any rate, must have realized the futility of his visit for he did not stay long. He reached Rivoli, near Turin, where the Duke of Savoy held his Court on 21 June. Morland had an audience with the Duke on 17 July when he presented the appeal of Cromwell in writing. The text of the speech in Latin which Morland delivered on this occasion is printed in the book that he wrote on his return.[12]

Morland was not immediately successful in his mission and left Turin on 19 July for Geneva, where he resided, during the autumn and winter, acting in concert with Dr. Pell, in dispensing the collected alms; in doing so they appeared to have relied upon co-religionists in the valleys. Morland spent much time in collecting material for, and planning, the history of the Waldensian Churches. Writing from Geneva in April 1656 to Thurloe, he says: 'I have sent you a project of my history enclosed'[13] which shows that the

---

[11] Vaughan, Robert, *The Protectorate of Oliver Cromwell*, 1839, Vol. I, p. 280.

[12] *History of the Evangelical Churches in the valleys of Piemont ... with a most naked and punctual relation of the late Bloudy Massacre in 1655 and the narrative of all the following transactions to ... 1658*. London, 1658.

[13] Vaughan, Robert, Vol. I, p. 379.

history had been premeditated and that this was part of his instructions, as was the case.

Another way in which Morland made use of his time was in acquiring greater knowledge of languages; he wrote on 3 June 1656: 'I take extreme delight in the High Dutch at present, having bent my studies lately to understand that language.'[14] As Italian was spoken at the Court of Savoy, Morland probably acquired some knowledge of that language also.

In August 1655, Morland was authorised to announce that the Duke, on the advice of the King of France, had granted an amnesty to the Waldenses and that the inhabitants, Protestant and Catholic, had sworn to live in amity. In September, Morland was ready to return to England, as he writes in a letter of 23rd of that month: 'I am preparing all things for my journey home,' but he was delayed for about a month by a high fever. On 23 October Thurloe wrote to him: 'supposing you have fully perfected the disposing of the last £500 among the poor people of Piedmont, His Highness [i.e. Cromwell] hath commanded me to signify to you that his pleasure is that you return to England.'[15] On 25 November he arrived in Lyons and on 9 December in Paris. On the 18th 'Mr. Morland with all his company' arrived at Dieppe. A few days later he reached England glad, no doubt, to be home for Christmas.

His mission had been successful, the persecution had been stopped, troops had been withdrawn from the valleys, prisoners released and Cromwell's influence had been established. We learn from the *History* (p. 594) that £38,097 had been collected. Of this sum Morland had dispensed £7,142 at Geneva and a further sum of £5,265 was distributed after his departure. Pell and Morland together had

[14] *Ibid.*, Vol. I, p. 417.
[15] *Loc. cit.*, Vol. II, pp. 3 and 58.

spent £9,501, the total of which is £21,908. What became of some of the balance of £16,000 odd we shall learn later.

A Select Committee of the House of Commons was appointed to receive Morland's report and on 7 January 1657, he records: 'Yesterday I gave the Committee for the valleys an account of those affairs in a discourse of an hour long.'[16] They issued a 'Certificate of the committee for Piemont concerning Mr. Morland's negociations for the protestants of the valleys' and Morland received the thanks of Parliament.[17]

On 21 May he records: 'I escaped death very narrowly,' presumably from an accident, but he gives no details.

The documents and materials that he had collected relating to the Waldenses (without sufficient discrimination, be it said, for he accepted the statement, as it will be observed Milton did also, that the sect dated back to apostolic times, instead of having been founded by Peter Waldo towards the beginning of the thirteenth century) found their way eventually by presentation of Morland to the Library of his own University, Cambridge, where they were lost sight of for many years, but eventually were brought to light in 1862 by Henry Bradshaw, the Librarian.[18]

The preparation of the *History* became one of Morland's preoccupations during the succeeding year. It was but natural that Cromwell, having succeeded abroad in his crusade, should be anxious that all the world should learn about it, especially with such a background of learning as Morland could lend to it. The volume was certainly well produced and obviously no expense was spared; it was

[16] *Loc. cit.*, Vol. II, p. 81.

[17] *Autobiography*, Appendix III.

[18] The MSS. are described in the *Catalogue of Manuscripts preserved in the Library of the University of Cambridge*, Vol. I, pp. 81–99, 548–552 and in Bradshaw's *Collected Papers*, pp. 1–15.

enriched with copper plates and last, but not least, with a
frontispiece portrait of himself engraved after Sir Peter Lely
by Pierre Lombart. This in itself strikes one as being the
outcome of vanity and conceit, or the act of one who wished
to push himself into notoriety. This is confirmed by the
dedication to Cromwell, which is fulsome, but hardly more
so than was then customary in such effusions. How Morland
was able to effect all this is shown by a minute of the
Council's proceedings of 5 May 1657: 'Morland to have
700 li. for the charge of paper, printing and cutting'
(i.e. engraving) 'of the mapps for two thousand coppies of
the History of ye Prostestants of ye valleyes of Piedmont,
he to have the benefit of printing the said History'. Was the
cost of the Lely portrait paid out of this?[19] Later, on 25
November (Vol. 11) this item appeared: 'to pay Sam Moreland 300L. for his pains from the interest on the loan of
the money collected.' This douceur was appointed to be
paid on 16 December.

Morland's services had been recognised already by
Cromwell appointing him by Letters Patent on 30 June
1656, one of the 'Clerks of His Highness's Signet', at a
salary of £150 per annum. It was not a large salary even for
those days, and on 31 August 1658, Morland begged
Thurloe for the office of 'Clerk of the Pells [Pells = parch-
ments] in the Exchequer,' vacant by the death the previous
day of Dennis Bond. This appeal evidently failing, he
presented 'a humble address' to Thurloe appealing for a
more remunerative post and drawing attention to his
poverty-stricken condition:[20] 'My signet fees have hardly
amounted the last quarter to above 7l. and one time with
another dos little more than mayntein my writing-clerck
and buy parchments. Of my sallary of 150l. per annum, I

[19] Cal. Stat. Pap. Dom. Commonwealth, Vol. 10, 1656–57.
[20] Burch, T., Collection of the State Papers of John Thurloe, Esq., 1742, p. 470.

will willingly loose one third to be free from the trouble of solliciting and waiting for the rest; and for the moytie of the Newes-book profitts, your lordshipp was so favourablie pleased to order mee to receive of Mr. Needham, hee hath so artificially delayed the payment thereof . . . that he is now in arreares with mee at least 280*l.* and has lately told mee plainly that hee will pay mee no more. Truly my lord these and the like things occasion mee many a pensive hour.' Attached is 'an abbreviat of my accompts with Mr. Need-ham' showing that from 22 May 1656, to 26 August 1658, Mr. Needham received 1280*l.* 13*s.* the moyety of this 635*l.* 6*s.* 6*d.* This does not reflect much credit on Morland's arithmetic.[21] In his position as Clerk of the Signet he says: 'I was admitted into the most intimat Affayrs of state where I had frequent opportunities of taking a clear view of all proceedings from [16]41 to [16]56 and so forwards for severall years.' It is known that Thurloe organised a secret service that, by all accounts, was most efficient, and in this Morland was partially engaged. His special task was the opening, copying and resealing of letters that passed through the Post Office; he became particularly expert in these operations as we shall see by details to be submitted later (see p. 96). What is important for the time being is that he was in a position to know a great deal of the plotting that was taking place on the Royalist side.

Besides his salary, Morland must have had other sources of income, as we shall see later, and was now in such com-fortable circumstances that he considered himself able to contemplate matrimony. His choice fell upon a lady who is described in the Naturalisation Bill brought into the House of Commons in 1662, as 'Susanne de Milleville, daughter of Daniel de Milleville, Baron de Boissay' in Normandy; actually he was 'Esquyor, Sieur de Boissay,' i.e. landed

[21] *Rept. D.K.P.R.* and Brit. Mus. *Stowe MS.,* 497.

gentleman. There are several places there named Boissay or Boissy, this particular one being known now as Boissay-pas-Londonières, a hamlet about nineteen m. S.E. of Dieppe in the present Département de la Seine Maritime.[22]

How and when Morland met the lady we do not know, but it is reasonable to suppose that it was in the course of his journey through France to Savoy in 1655. The De Millevilles were a Protestant family and would naturally be interested in Morland's errand on behalf of the Vaudois. It will be recalled that on his return journey he crossed the Channel from Dieppe and no doubt he took that opportunity to renew acquaintance with the lady and her parents. The date of his marriage is fixed by a letter to Thurloe from 'Boissay, in Normandy', 27 August 1657, in which he says: 'It is now about a fortnight since I set out from Whitehall to this place in order to the changing of my condition.'[23] The honeymoon was apparently spent at Boissay and was prolonged by difficulties in getting back to England. Writing to Pell at Zurich on 22 September, Morland says he had been a fortnight 'in expectation first of a ship and now of a wind to convey me to England.' A month later he was back in Whitehall and, writing again, (22 October) to Pell he says: 'Saturday night last I arrived here safe with my dear wife.' He had been 'stopped six weeks for want of a ship'[24]—a vivid commentary on the delays of travel in the seventeenth century. Once back at work, we gather from further letters to Pell that he was kept very busy by Thurloe.

Where they set up house we do not know. Certainly in 1660 he had 'a Countrey house a little beyond Bow,' probably the equivalent of our country cottage. This does

[22] 'I am indebted to M. Pierre Antoine Daon of Briouze, Orne, for identifying the spot and for information about the Milleville family, a representative of which is still living at Boissay.' Rhys Jenkins.

[23] Vaughan, Robert, Vol. II, p. 236.

[24] *Loc. cit.*, p. 26.

not tally with the statement in his *Autobiography* that at this time he was flourishing. He says, 'I lived in greater plenty than ever I did since the King's Restauration having a house well furnish't, a sufficient number of servants and attendants, a very good Coach and horses in my stables, a revenue of above a Thousand pound per annum to mainteyn it, and several hundreds of pounds of ready money by mee; and a beautiful young woman to my wife for a companion.'

His wife would be sure to have brought a 'dot' with her and this may have helped. She seems to have been a woman with great ideas of her own importance and proud of her descent 'from a Noble Family in Normandy.' There were several children of the marriage; we know of three: Samuel, born in 1662 or 1663; Susannah, born in 1666 and baptised at Norwood, 28 February; and Anne, whose burial at Kensington Church, 2 March 1670, is recorded.

However, we anticipate, and must now return to White-hall and to the intrigues that were going on there. In these Morland was inextricably mixed and his conduct has led to charges being levelled against him by his enemies of being a spy and a traitor because he went over to the Royalist side. We shall try to sift the evidence and first look at it from his own angle. In his *Autobiography* he says: 'I was an ey and ear witnes of Dr. Hewet's being inhumanely trepann'd to death[25] (together with several other persons of quality) by Thurlo and his agents.' Dr. John Hewet (1614–58) was an episcopal clergyman who had been indefatigable in enlisting partisans in the plot of April 1658 against Cromwell to place Charles II on the throne. Hewet was brought to trial, condemned and executed along with Sir Henry Slingsby on 8 June on Tower Hill.

Another intrigue which was being carried on was that

[25] The word 'trepan' meant entrap (by a trick), ensnare.

through the instrumentality of Sir Richard Willis. He was a Royalist, who had been created a Baronet by Charles I and was deep in the counsels of his son in exile. Willis appears to have been suborned by Thurloe as early as 1656, so that while carrying on correspondence with Charles, Willis disclosed to Thurloe everything that he learnt in the comings and goings with Charles by messenger and otherwise. Morland states that the intrigue was going on 'from a year before Cromwell's death' and eventually it developed into a design to assassinate Charles. He was to be invited to come over to England with his two brothers and a few more attendants in a single ship to a port in the south of England, thence to be conducted to the isolated, moated country house of Weston Hanger (Westenhanger 4 m. N.W. of Hythe) in Kent, where they were promised to be received and supported by a force of five hundred foot soldiers and, a day after arrival, by a further force of two thousand horse. Actually the men were to be stationed in the woods surrounding the house and at an appointed signal they were to rush in and quickly dispatch Charles, so that no one in particular could be charged with the deed. Morland states that he was privy to the design.[26] He was at his desk in Thurloe's office, apparently asleep. He was spied by Cromwell, who drew his poniard and was dissuaded from dispatching Morland on the spot only by the earnest solicitation of Thurloe, who assured Cromwell that Morland had sat up two nights together and was certainly fast asleep.

Morland pondered on the oaths of supremacy and allegiance to the King that he had sworn when he entered Winchester College, and no doubt some respect for royalty, though strained by the King's disregard of the Constitution from early days, still lingered in his mind. On the other

[26] Welwood, *Memoirs*, 1700, p. 11.

c

hand, he reflected upon the allegiance he owed to Cromwell, the latter's settled government at home and his strong policy abroad. Morland's version of what took place, although penned long after the event and coloured by the passage of time is this: 'I took at last a firm resolution to do my native prince and the Rightfull Heir to the Crown all the service that should lay in my power.'[27] He then gives a long circumstantial but not altogether lucid account of the course of events. He says that he sent money surreptitiously to the King, who was reduced to pawning even his jewels and plate. In doing so, he hazarded his official position and risked imprisonment or deportation to the Barbados, which is what Thurloe threatened for anyone he suspected of being a traitor. Morland argued that his conduct could not have been motivated by hope of reward or honour, for at that time, if it had been his aim, he had opportunities of obtaining greater sums by embezzlement or treason. With the help of Major Henshaw, Morland warned the King of the conspiracy against his life. The King had sent him two letters which he attached to the statement, but these are now missing from the Lambeth MS.

Charles is said to have received Morland's disclosure of the plot when he was pulling on his boots to set out on the journey to England; instead of doing so, he sent to Willis evasive and procrastinating letters. The latter smelt a rat and believing that Morland was the only one who could have been privy to the plot confronted the latter to his great confusion; a duel was only averted by the prompt action of Morland drawing a pistol on Willis.

A complete change came over the scene with the death of Cromwell, which occurred on 3 September 1658. Like so many men of great powers, he was unwilling to delegate authority; thus the provision he had made to ensure the

[27] *Autobiography*, Appendix III.

continuity of the Commonwealth was inadequate. One provision in particular failed; that was his scheme of leaving
the Protectorate on the shoulders of his son, Richard. The
latter failed entirely, because he had neither the desire nor
the capacity for the office. Richard's accession was received
without overt opposition; soon, however, there were
indications of discord in the Army. While some were content
with a Protectorate, others wished for a Republic. It was the
same in the Council of State which, no more than the Army,
was desirous of a Parliament.

Now supervened a period of violent flux of opinion and
intrigue. The Parliamentary Army since the retirement of
Lord Fairfax had become the 'happy hunting ground' of
enthusiasts whose views on Government where anarchial
and, for the period, impracticable. True, the fear of religious
and political domination by Rome, which had been the
prevailing feeling of the generation that had fought in the
Civil Wars, and had been the mainspring of the force that
had enabled Parliament and Cromwell to triumph over the
King, had not ceased to exist; yet it was felt that religious
freedom was safeguarded. Germany, since the Peace of
Westphalia 1648, was assured of the same freedom, and
France for the time being was a tolerant power, thanks to
the intervention of Cromwell in foreign affairs. 'In England,
ever increasing numbers of the new generation shared
neither the prejudices of the Cavaliers, nor the fanaticism of
the Puritan, above all they were weary of perpetual strife.'[28]

Among the latter category was Morland and from this
time there began the swing of the pendulum. However, the
Treasury was exhausted and an attempt to borrow money
from the French King was naturally unsuccessful. It was
decided, therefore, to summon Parliament in order that
supplies might be voted; the opening took place in January

[28] Fitzmaurice, Lord Edmond, *Life of Sir William Petty*, 1895, p. 100.

1659 and at once there was dissension between the Commons and the Lords. The Army intervened and Richard was forced to dissolve Parliament on 22 April. The remnant or 'Rump' of the Long Parliament was then summoned and this body declared for a Government by 'no single person' and 'without a House of Peers.' At the same time Thurloe was relieved of his duties and Morland must have felt that his own position was precarious; indeed it is probable that he too was dismissed.

In May, Richard, withdrawing altogether from the strife, retired into Hampshire. Again there were disputes between the Army and Parliament. In October the government was taken into the hands of a Committee of Safety. Was it strange that men's minds should turn to the King in exile and that the pendulum should begin to swing in his direction?

How precarious Morland's position was we learn from gossip set down in correspondence between the Marquis du Chastel, the French Ambassador and M. de Vaux in London. The latter writing to the Marquis, 30 April 1659[29] says: 'It is time that *you* and the Earl of Arundel looked to your safety and *Morland* and *his wife*.' The Marquis in his replies says on May 11th, '*Morland is nothing*;' again on 25 May, 'It goes ill with *Morland and his wife*,' and on 22 June, '*Morland and his wife* are in the country, he is quite out of employment.'

This may well have nerved him to take the plunge; we shall never know the real truth, however, for, alluding in the *Autobiography* to these passages in his life he says: 'Being willing to carry the rest into the grave with mee . . . there to bee buried in oblivion.'

Although Thurloe was reappointed in 1660, Morland must have seen the red light, and he decided to go over to the King. The upshot of it was that on 16 May 1660, he

---

[29] *Cal. Stat. Pap. Dom.*, Commonwealth, Vol. 12.

crossed over to Breda in Holland, where the King was then residing, along with a stream of other persons on similar errands. Charles received Morland graciously, created him a Knight upon the spot and promised, so Morland's wife believed, 'to give mee the Gartar and make her [his wife] a Dutchess.' This sounds so extravagant that one wonders that Morland should have been so gullible as to believe the promise, even if it were actually made. There is no doubt that his wife believed it and would have welcomed the prospect, but what Morland wanted, it seems, was a fat sinecure; indeed we shall see later that he kept in view before him consistently the main chance and never lost an opportuniy of securing a pension or a grant of money.

Pepys records in his Diary, 13 May 1660:[30] 'I heard . . . how Mr. Morland was knighted by the King this week and that the King did give the reason of it openly, that it was for giving him intelligence all the time he was clerk to Secretary Thurloe.' The actual date on which the knighthood was conferred was May 20th. One wonders at the King making this announcement for, even if true, it did not resound to the credit of either and an ostensible reason would have served.

When revealing the conspiracy against Charles's life and engaging to serve him, Morland made it clear that it was on condition 'that I might never be call'd to bear witness against any of the conspirators, if upon his restauration they should happen to bee arraigned at the barr of justice.' Later when Sir Harry Vane was brought to trial for high treason, the Attorney General pressed Morland to appear against him, but the latter would not do so.

Charles reached Dover on 26 May and on the 29th, a day to be remembered subsequently and kept as a holiday as Royal Oak Day as late as the author's boyhood, entered

[30] This and succeeding quotations from Pepys are taken from Wheatley's Edition of the *Diary*, 1926.

London in triumph. The gossip is that he was said to have spent the preceding night at Morland's house at Bow, by the side of his mistress Barbara Villiers, afterwards Lady Castlemaine.[31]

On 11 August 1660 Morland was created a Baronet and Gentleman of the Privy Chamber. Pepys, speaking of the voyage from Holland under date 15 May says, 'Mr. Morland, now Sir Samuel, was here on board but I do not find that my Lord (the Earl of Sandwich) or anybody did give him any respect, he being looked upon by him and all men as a knave.' Evidently Morland was anxious to remove or live down this bad impression and three months later we find that he took an opportunity of telling Pepys the full story of the incident, which the latter sets down as follows:

14 August 1660: 'Thence to the Privy Seale again where Sir Samuel Morland came with a baronet's grant to pass which the King had given him to make money of. Here he staied a great while; and told me the whole manner of his serving the King in the time of the Protectorate; and how Thurloe's bad usage made him to do it; how he discovered Sir R. Willis's plot and how he hath sunk his fortune to the King; and that now the King hath given him a pension of £500 per annum out of the Post Office for life and the benefit of two baronets; all which do make me begin to think that he is not so much a fool that I took him to be.'

Pepys evidently did not see anything amiss in this conduct, and might have acted in a similar way himself, had he been in Morland's place. Nothing in the sale of honours that we have known in this and the last century reached such a depth as this. The baronetcy had been conferred on 18 July and as some territorial designation for the dignity is

---

[31] cf. Imbert-Terry, H. M., *A Misjudged Monarch*, 1917, p. 96, and Dasent, H. J., *Private Life of Charles II*, 1927, p. 91.

necessary, the baronetcy was 'of Sulhampstead Bannister in the County of Berks.' This was really an empty phrase as Morland possessed no land there. It appears that in the grant the Heralds' fees were specially remitted as we learn from the following: '1660 Oct. 22. Lord Treasurer's Warrent to the Auditor of the Receipt *et al.* to levy a tally importing the payment of the Baronet fee of £1,095 by Sir Samuel Morland.'[32]

These honours would have been appropriate if Morland had possessed an income to support them, but this was far from being the case for he was penniless. We have this despairing petition from him to the King, not dated but probably July, 1660, as follows:[33]

'Samuel Morland petitions for some exemplary mark of favour, whereby he may bear up against his difficulties, or some small sum to find him and his family bread in some remote place, where it may never be known what his hazards, services and hopes have been. Is pursued by the implacable hatred of his enemies, has no place of credit and is poorer by 2000*l* that when he entered the service; his wife has lost 10,000*l* by not enticing him to go to France, where her uncle would have made her his heir; is a scorn to his enemies who point at him as a perfidious fellow who betrayed his own masters and will have a spy's reward; and those who love and have heard His Majesty's gracious expressions concerning him, think he has forfeited his favour so that he is ashamed to show his head.'

This is borne out to some extent by what Pepys has to say in his diary on 14 May writing about the voyage to England. The result was that he was granted a pension amounting to the sum of £500 p.a. secured on the revenues of the Post Office. He was hot-foot in announcing his good fortune to

[32] *Cal. Treas. Books*, 1660–67, No. 78.
[33] *Cal. Stat. Pap.*, 1660–61, XX, No. 37, p. 336.

Pepys, for the grant was not passed till 22 August and the warrant was not made out till October: '1660 Oct. 4th Warrant to pay out of the Post Office for the 1st quarter to Michaelmas last on Sir Samuel Morland's pension for £500 per an.'[34]

The succeeding warrant was on 11 October 'money warrant for £125 (by tallies on Henry Bishop, esq. Post Master General) to Sir Samuel Morland for one quarter to September 29 last on his annuity as by letters patent of Aug. 22nd last: with dormant warrant for continuation of same in future.'

The succeeding part of the story is a sordid one: 'being forced to live at a great expence and lay out great sums in taking out patents and riding at the coronation &c. and so run myself in debt, there was one sent to mee to give mee an Alarm that the Duke of York would have the post office settled on him and my pension would bee lost and I should do prudently to sell it, and there was a chapman for it, which was Sir Arthur Slingsby, who had it for a sum much beneath its value, and as I heard afterwards hee bought it for the Lady Green, with the King's Money.'

This is a revelation both of credulity on the part of Morland and of chicanery and intrigue on the part of those surrounding him which can hardly be credited. We can easily imagine that the King, surrounded as he was by greedy courtiers, asking for sinecures or preferment, should have promised more than he could perform, but it does seem singular that instead of finding or creating some office of profit for Morland in the public service, for which his abilities had already qualified him, the King should have taken this course. It may be that Morland realized that he was no match in duplicity for those around him and aimed rather at getting out of the atmosphere of intrigue by some sinecure.

[34] *Cal. Treas. Books*, 1660–67, No. 72.

The extraordinary upsurge of new ideas and opinions between 1640 and 1660 in England is not always recognised. During these twenty years more social and political ideas were formulated, debated and tried out experimentally than in any similar period in the country's history. It was the birth of a new era in nearly every sphere, but possibly the greatest change was achieved in the regard of science towards life; the Baconian philosophy became the touchstone of the age. A young man, especially one who had been at a university like Cambridge and had subsequently seen a good deal of the larger world, could not have failed to have been deeply influenced.

At any rate from now onwards a definite change in the career of Morland ensued and he now took up invention and research. To these the next chapters will, in the main, be devoted.

CHAPTER III

OUTBURST OF INVENTION
1661-75

Inventions and Devices; Calculating Machines; Perpetual Almanack; Cipher Writing; Gunpowder Engine; Commissioner of Excise; Speaking Trumpet; Inclined Tube Barometer; Leases Vauxhall House

'Now finding myself disappoynted of all preferment and of any real estate, I betook myself to the Mathematicks and Experiments such as I found pleased the King's Fancy.' Thus relates Morland in his *Autobiography*. (See Appendix III).

It is well-known that Charles II was a great patron of science and the arts, showing this by many of his actions; perhaps Morland thought that by turning to mathematics and practical science he would retain the King's favour.

Here we might interpose that it was the fashion of the time to propose 'inventions and devices' which were claimed by their authors as being within their knowledge to compass. We can instance, besides the Marquis of Worcester's well-known *Century of Inventions*, 1666, the earlier efforts of William Bourne, 1578, Ralph Rabbards, c. 1590, Edmund Gentill, c. 1594, and Sir Bevis Bulmer, 1644.

One would have thought that, had Morland shown any aptitude for or had any urge to study practical science, it would have manifested itself earlier in his career. He was now about thirty-six years of age; as compared with this, a study of the lives of inventors shows that a man's most prolific period of invention begins about a decade earlier than this age and closes about the time when he is forty. Beyond a statement by Samuel Hartlib in a letter to Pell dated 14 December 1655, that Morland had informed him that he had profoundly studied the art of flying and had 'made many experiments in it,'[35] there is nothing to show that he did anything in mechanical matters until after the Restoration.

Morland in his *Autobiography* twice makes this statement about turning to mathematics, so that he must have thought it important; perhaps, therefore, we may examine this phase of his life first, and later turn to his other inventions, taking them as far as possible in chronological order. We shall find them quite a remarkable catalogue. Judging from his statement, one might be pardoned for supposing that Morland had done some original work in mathematics; but, if so, we have not come across any mention of it in the letters of his friends, such as those of John Pell, or elsewhere. It was the vogue for mathematicians publicly to set problems for solution—a kind of challenge from one individual to his fellows—and thus excite emulation, not only in this country but also in Europe; we do not find that Morland even did this. Late in life, i.e. in 1688, writing to Thomas Tenison, (1636–1715), later Bishop of Lincoln, and afterwards Archbishop of Canterbury, he had begun 'to consider that perhaps I might do the public some kind of service, during this my retired life, by explayning in a new manner and method, the first six books of Euclid and reducing them to common use and practice, and making all things plain and easy to the meanest capacity which is a thing that in my opinion would bee of excellent and singular use, as well for all publick schools as for all young students in the universities.' Nothing came of it, however, and it was left for

[35] Vaughan, Robert, Vol. II, p. 429.

Robert Simson in 1756 to carry out this idea in his well-known edition of Euclid.

Morland must have been fully alive to the fact that he could not make any sort of a living from the study of mathematics, or even of science in general; the indigence to which men like Thomas Lydyat and his own friend, Pell in his latter days, were reduced, was sufficient to disprove the idea. Morland might have taken up teaching and opened an Academy for boys, as did his brother Martin when ejected from his living. The only other way was to treat the subject as a hobby, while in the enjoyment of a college fellowship, a living in the Church, or a private income. The first two, in his case, were foregone already, but apparently he thought the third alternative practicable. Hence his persistence in hunting after pensions, offices and preferment, which we shall have to record as we go along.

What Morland did in regard to mathematics was to devote a good deal of time to the construction of a calculating machine. It is hardly hazarding a guess if we state that his attention was drawn to the subject by the work of the celebrated mathematician Blaise Pascal, (1623–62), who had devised his machine when only nineteen years of age, at the time when his family were at Rouen, in order to assist his father, the Supervisor of Taxes there, in statistical work, involving addition and subtraction of sums of money. It is more than probable that Morland first heard of Pascal's machine when in Sweden. Queen Christina was an accomplished although erratic woman; as we have said she was a great patron of arts and sciences and attracted to her court such men as Grotius, Salmasius and Descartes. Pascal sent one of his machines to her in 1649 with a letter and this might well have been one of the curiosities shown to distinguished visitors like the Ambassador and his suite. It is also certain that Morland saw a machine in Paris when he passed through there in 1655, for several such machines had been made there by that time under Pascal's direction and subsequently.

Previous to the latter's time, in the classical period, calculation—addition and subtraction—was done by the aid of calculi or pebbles, later embodied in a frame or abacus. In 1617 John Napier of Merchiston, near Edinburgh, invented a device consisting essentially of multiplication tables, written on slips of wood or bone, which could be put together in such a way that any desired product could be read off: they became known as Napier's 'bones' or 'rods'. The great advance made by Pascal was in the introduction of wheelwork to effect the operations more quickly and certainly. A six-figure machine made in Paris in 1652 inscribed: *'Esto probati instrumenti symbolum hoc: Blasius Pascal, Arvernus, Inventor, 20 mai 1652'* is still in existence and is now preserved in Paris at the Conservatoire des Arts et Métiers; we would fain believe that it was this actual machine which Morland saw. It is in the highest degree improbable that Morland should have met Pascal, as the latter's 'second conversion' took place in 1654; thenceforward he devoted himself to a religious life. The machine mentioned above was for simple addition and subtraction but Pascal also, as said above, made modifications to suit livres, sols and deniers.

Morland's machine, of which several examples are still in existence,—for instance, two at the Science Museum, London, and one at the Old Ashmolean Museum, Oxford,—is a compact little apparatus made in brass, 4 in. by 3 in. and less than ¼ in. thick. The front plate is silvered and engraved *'Samuel Morland Inventor* (1666' (see Plate I). In a little book entitled *'The Description and Use of Two Arithmetick Instruments'*, 1673 but written as internal evidence shows in 1671, he says it was issued 'By the Importunity of his very good

Friends' and he describes the machine as a 'new and most useful instrument for addition and subtraction of pounds, shillings, pence, and farthings without charging the memory, disturbing the mind, or exposing the operator to any uncertainty; which no method hitherto published can justly pretend to.'

It consists of two sets of wheelwork, the upper set registering from units to ten thousands and the lower registering from pence to pounds. The wheels are divided and numbered appropriately. A stylus was provided to turn the wheels till the number desired is seen through a slot or window on the face of the cover over the wheel. A counting disc above each is engaged once per revolution by a tooth on the edge of the wheel. Addition is effected by turning the wheels clockwise and subtraction by turning them anticlockwise.[36]

In the volume mentioned, after dealing with the adding and subtracting machine, Morland goes on to describe with four engraved plates, which we reproduce (see Plates II and III) a multiplying machine entitled '*Machina Nova Cyclologica Pro Multiplicatione. Or, a new Multiplying-Instrument: Invented and humbly presented to the King's Most Excellent Majesty, Charles II. By S. Morland 1666.*' One of these machines was subsequently presented by Morland to the Grand Duke of Tuscany and is now in the Museo di Storia della Scienza, Florence. (see Plate IV) It is inscribed: '*Henricus Sutton et Samuel Knibb Londini fecerunt 1664. Equite aurato et Baronetto inventa anno salutis 1666. Nec non Serenissimo Principi Cosmo III Magno Duci Etruriae humillime oblata anno salutis 1679*'. The principle underlying the operation of the instrument is the same as that used in Napier's 'Rods', except that the latter are replaced by rotatable discs and the

[36] Baxandall, D. A., Catalogue of the Collections in the Science Museum, London, *Mathema ics. I: Calculating Machines and Instruments.* 1926.

figures are arranged near the edges of the discs at opposite ends of diameters. The machine served also for the extraction of square, cube, and square-square roots. A full description will be found in the Science Museum catalogue.[36]

Morland issued on page 12 of his book 'A CAUTION to all who desire to make Use of either of these INSTRUMENTS.

'If any person desire to have either of these Instruments exactly made, and so as it may be serviceable for many years, He may bespeak it of Mr. Humphry Adamson, living at present at the house of Jonas Moor, Esq: in the Tower, who is the onely Workman that ever as yet could be found by the Author to perform the said Instrument, with that exactness that is absolutely necessary for such Operations.'

It will be recalled that the Tower was then an Armoury and thus may be explained how it was that artisans and facilities existed there for making these machines.

May it be supposed that the machine with which Morland calculated the table 'Touching the Quadrature of the circle' that he gives in his *Élévation des Eaux* 1685, to be referred to below, was one of his own?

This, however, does not exhaust Morland's versatility, for he invented a trigonometrical calculating machine, two examples of which we know to be in existence. One is in the Science Museum, London, and was formerly the property of Charles Babbage, F.R.S. (see Plate VI). On the inside of the lid is this inscription: '*Machina Cyclologica Trigonometrice Quâ Tribus datis, reliqua omnia in Triangulis Planis Quæsita faciliter atque unico intuitu expediuntur—a Samuele Morlando inventa—Anno Salutis MDCLXIII.*' This machine is signed '*Henricus Sutton et Samuel Knibb Londini fecerunt 1664.*' The other is in the Museo di Storia della Scienza, Florence. (see Plate VII). It is signed: '*Johannes Marke Londini fecit 1670*' and the lid of the box bore the same inscription as the

machine in London. If the dates are correct it is remarkable
that it should have been made before the simpler adding and
subtracting machine. It provides a means of rapidly constructing triangles to scale from given data by using graduated rods and circles. Problems in plain trigonometry,
ordinarily solved by plotting on paper, can be readily solved
by this instrument. Sine, cosine, or tangent of any angle
may be read off at once; multiplication and division can be
performed by employing the graphical method of similar
triangles. A full description of the instrument in the Science
Museum is given in the Catalogue quoted above.

Apparently the machines attracted some little notice but
the man in the street was not impressed, as is so usual when
a new invention is brought out. Pepys saw one at a dinner
and this is his observation:

14 March 1668: ' . . . and there, among many other things
my Lord [i.e. Hinchingbroke] had Sir Samuel Morland's
late invention for casting up of sums of £.s.d. which is very
pretty but not very useful.' Robert Hooke was another one
who disparaged them. In his Diary 31 January 1672/3 he
records: 'Saw Sir S. Morland's Arithmetic engine Very
silly—', but then Hooke was a rival inventor.

The machines were advertised for sale in the *London
Gazette*, as witness the following advertisement which
appeared in the issue of 16–20 April 1668: 'Sir Samuel Morland has found out two very usefull instruments; the one
serving for addition and substraction of any numbers of
Pounds, Shillings, Pence and Farthings or of any other
coins, Weights, and Measures . . . the other for the ready
performance of Multiplication and Division, together with
the Extraction of the Square and Cube Roots and that to
any number of Places required.' The time was not ripe for
the extended use of such machines because the need had
hardly yet been felt. Still more to the point is that methods

of interchangeable manufacture, which alone could make possible the production of such machines on any considerable scale and at any reasonable price, had not then been thought of, much less developed; nevertheless we can say with confidence that Morland's machines marked a distinct advance in design and construction. Had Morland done no more than this, he would have deserved credit for having made the calculating machine available for general use and of such a size that it could be carried conveniently in the pocket.

The *'Perpetual Almanack and several Useful Tables'* that were included by Morland in his book on the *'Arithmetick Instruments'* 1673, call only for brief mention, as they were of the kind we are familiar with nowadays, although in his time they were a rarity. It may be mentioned that in the copy of the Almanack in the British Museum Library there is inserted a copy of 'A Perpetuall Almanack invented by S. Morland, 1650,' on a single sheet printed from a copperplate; very likely this was the precursor of the larger Almanack. It looks as if it was intended to be carried in the pocket, for which its size is suitable. At any rate it indicates the date by which Morland had turned his attention to the subject of almanacks.

The perpetual almanack and tables afterwards became what we might call a standard work; it was published by John Playford (1613–93) under the title *'Vade Mecum or the Necessary Companion* containing 1. Sir S. Morland's Perpetual Almanack in Copper Plate with many useful tables proper thereto . . . London 1679' and ran into twenty-two editions. In the preface Playford says: 'The Perpetual Almanack was the ingenious invention of that great Improver of Art, and Encourager of Artists, Sir Samuel Morland.' On p. 137 Playford gives 'Sir Samuel Morland's tables for the Ready Casting up of any Number of Guinneys, at any rate from

D

Eighteen-Pence to Two Shillings' meaning by that, at the rates of 21s. 6d. rising to 22s. to the guinea.[37]

Another work by Morland, allied in character to what has gone before, may be mentioned here. It is his *Doctrine of Interest both simple and compound explained*, published by him in 1679. In it he animadverts on previous tables as being incorrect. All the operations shown in the book are performed by decimal arithmetic, which he strongly recommends and he gives the rules relative to this method. We have to remember that decimals had not yet come into general use, so that this shows Morland's sagacity. On page 203 'the *Author* of this little Book hopes That the manifold Errors in the Calculations of other Writers, will occasion a more kind acceptance of his more than ordinary care and diligence in all the foregoing Tables.' From this it is not too much to infer that he used his 'Arithmetick Machine' in recalculating the figures.

As a side issue to his studies in 'mathematicks' it is convenient to mention here that in 1666 Morland published a *New Method in Cryptography*, probably the outcome of his experiences when censoring correspondence during the Protectorate. The cipher was simply one dial concentric with another, so that the code letters on the rim could be

---

[37] The guinea was first issued, nominally as a 20s. piece, in 1663. At this time silver was standard money and gold coins circulated at varying values in terms of silver. (The money of account—£ s d—was silver money: £1 stood not for a gold coin or a note but for 20s. of current silver money). Since the guinea was undervalued in terms of silver, at the time of issue, it soon rose to 22s. Thereafter it circulated at a premium (over 20s.) which varied from 1s. 6d. to 3s. or even more, according to the relative value of gold with respect to silver. (Owing to the defective state of the silver money, the premium was as much as 10s. for a time in 1695). Hence there was a need for tables from which one could rapidly ascertain the value in £ s d of any number of guineas at a given premium.

In 1717, on the advice of Sir Isaac Newton, the guinea was definitely, and finally tarriffed at 21s. After this, gold became the standard monetary metal in place of silver. When the sovereign was introduced in 1816 its weight was made exactly 20/21 of that of the guinea. (Professor Douglas Dickinson).

read off; similarly at the other end, if the two agreed-upon letters were placed radially, decoding was equally easy. Any number of combinations, up to twenty-six, was possible. Such a simple method is easily solved and has been superseded by much more difficult methods. Apparently the volume was produced at the public expense for in 1667 we find 'bill of expenses about the circular cypher and about his last invention, printing 500 copies about its use, plates, paper, etc. total £272.10.7.'[38] It is possible that this bill covers the expenses of preparing the volume on the '*Arithmetick Instruments*' which the second title page states was presented to Charles II in 1666.

Gunpowder Engine: If there was one matter more than another at this period that called for inventive genius, it was improved means of raising water for the supply of dwellings and for draining mines. It was natural therefore that Morland should have joined the considerable number of persons whose minds were engrossed in trying to improve the means used hitherto—animal power, wind and water mills, actuating rag-and-chain or bucket pumps. This subject was one to which Morland returned again and again and effected improvements principally in the construction of the pump itself.

His first attempt, the earliest of its kind, was to employ the explosive power of gunpowder. In 1661 he petitioned the King for the grant of a patent for his invention of 'An Engine for the Raising of Water out of any Mines or Pits in greater quantities, shorter time and with much lesse help than has ever yet been practised or heard of.' The King ordered a bill to be prepared for his signature to grant a patent for the invention, which was described in somewhat greater detail and with the significant words inserted in the margin: 'and by the force of Aire and Powder conjointly.'

[38] *Cal. Stat. Pap. Dom.*, Chas. II, 230, No. 66.

In the author's opinion these words were inserted by the King himself, who knew that many other persons, for example the Marquis of Worcester, were trying to achieve the same result and that the means of doing so should be narrowly defined so as not to restrict inventions employing other agencies. The words show us that it was a gunpowder engine—an internal combustion engine and the first of its kind.[39] We do not know of any experiments having been made by Morland; no doubt sufficient were made to convince him that the idea was impracticable. The fact remains that, although the warrant for the patent was made out, he did not take the final steps to secure the grant. Twenty years passed before Morland returned to the idea of making a heat engine but this time employing fire and water to secure the end in view; meanwhile he was fully employed on other inventions, of which we must give some account.

It is of interest to note that it was not till thirteen years after Morland's attempt, viz. in 1674, that Christiaan Huygens and Denis Papin in the laboratory of the Royal Society of France 'were trying experiments with the air pump with a little gunpowder to lift 1,000 lb. weight,'[40] but again without success.

A little gossip about Morland and his wife can be gathered from the inimitable Pepys. Under date 13 August 1663, he jots down: 'Met with Mr. Hoole[41] my old acquaintance of Magdalen, and walked with him in the Parke, discussing chiefly of Sir Samuel Morland whose lady has gone into France. It seems he buys ground and a farm in the country and lays out money upon building and God knows what! So that most of the money he sold his pension of £500 per

[39] *Cal. Stat. Pap. Dom.*, Charles II.
[40] *Diary of Robert Hooke*, Ed. Robinson & Adams, 1935. p. 104.
[41] William Hoole, of Walkeringham, Notts., was admitted to Magdalene College June 1648; how he was employed at this time we cannot say, but he must have been well known to Morland who may have been his Tutor.

annum for, to Sir Arthur Slingsby is believed to be gone. It seems he hath very great promises from the King and Hoole hath seen some of the King's letters under his own hand promising him many things (and among others the Order of the Garter as Sir Samuel says) but his lady thought it below her to ask anything of the King first coming believing the King would do it of himself, when as Hoole do really think if he had asked to be Secretary of State at the King's first coming, he might have had it. And the other day at her going into France, she did speak largely to the King herself, how her husband hath failed of what his Majesty had promised and she was sure intended him: and the King did promise still, as he is a King and a gentleman, to be as good as his word in a little time to a tittle, but I never believe it.'

This gossip is all confirmed in the *Autobiography*, so that it is probably only a rechauffé of what Morland himself had related to Pepys and Hoole in turn. The King's apparent ingratitude seems to have rankled pretty deeply. Further gossip by Pepys goes to show how extravagant and improvident Morland's and his wife's married life appeared to outsiders, thus:

25 November 1664: 'I by coach to the Change and took up Mr. Jennings along with me (my old acquaintance) he telling me the mean manner that Sir Samuel Morland lives near him, in a house he hath bought and laid out money for, in all to the value of £1,200, but is believed to be a beggar; and so I ever thought he would be.' Possibly this, the house mentioned, is the one at Bow previously described.

Another piece of gossip, showing a good deal of 'swank' on the part of Sir Samuel and his Lady, is revealed by this entry in the *Diary*:

11 December 1664: 'Lord's Day. In the afternoon I to the French Church . . . here was Sir Samuel Morland and his

Lady very fine, with two footmen in new liverys (the church taking much notice of them) and going into their Coach after sermon with great gazing.'

It will be remembered that Pepys's wife was, like Lady Morland, a Frenchwoman, and this explains why he was at the French Church.

Lady Morland seems to have gone to and from France fairly frequently. In 1668, 23 September, we find: 'Certificate[42] by Jos. Hinton, Luke Rugeley and Thos. Willis that Lady Moreland has the dropsy and is considered hardly curable; and as she has a desire to return to France, her native country, they conceive the air may be of advantage to her health. With note that a pass is required for Lady Moreland and her two children, and 2 maid servants and a foot-boy.'

The number in her suite would indicate a condition of some affluence, while the cost of travelling must also have been considerable. Six days later the desired pass was issued. We do not know when Lady Morland returned to this country, but the disease evidently proved fatal for she died soon after, possibly in childbirth.

In 1668 Morland was appointed Secretary to the Commissioners for Ireland. We know of this from a letter from John Verney to Sir Ralph Verney:[43]

26 August 1668: . . . 'Yesterday was the first day the Commissioners for Ireland sat . . . Sir Samuel Morland is Secretary of the Commission.' What were the duties of the office, their extent or how long the appointment lasted we have not learnt.

In 1669 he was appointed one of the Commissioners of Appeal in Excise at a salary of £200 p.a. and in the following year, 24 June 1670, he was, shall we say, promoted to be a Commissioner of Excise with a salary of £500 p.a. He held

[42] *Cal. Stat. Pap. Dom.* 1667–68.
[43] *Hist. MSS. Comm.* Vol. V, 486b. Sir R. Verney's MSS.

the appointment—we presume it was not a sinecure but we do not know—till the 29 September 1674 when he was succeeded by Sir J. James.

About this time, Morland seems to have been regarded in the light of an engineer, for such he really was. He made a translation of Blaise François Comte de Pagan's *Traité des Fortifications*, 1645, simply reducing French to English measures and 'converted into Hercotechtonick-Lines' but without adding anything material to it. This work he published in 1672 and Hooke in his *Diary* notes the purchase of a copy. The work must have been on the way for some time for, as indicating the date when he first gave his attention to the subject, on page 65 there is a copperplate engraving entitled 'Lineae Hercotectonicae Novae', dedicated to Charles II and dated 1666. We couple this with an entry in the State Papers[44]:

'Minute of a grant to Sir Samuel Morland and his heirs of the sole making and vending of a medal, the workmanship to be done by the Mint Officers on their furnishing the metal into which medal is contrived a new method of fortifications instituted by the King with the inscription "Methodus Hercotectonica Nova" of which the figure and rules[45] are annexed.' An example of this medal is to be found in the Coins and Medals Department of the British Museum.

About 1670 there was a proposal to open up the River Ouse in Norfolk for navigation. Lord Arlington under date August 1670, wrote as follows: 'Sir Samuel Morland is with us [i.e. at Euston Hall near Thetford] and will view the river also, and when I have his opinion I will call the company [i.e. the Mayor and Citizens of Thetford] together again and try and agree upon something.'[46] Nothing appears

[44] *Cal. Stat. Pap. Dom.*, 1668/9, p. 653.
[45] These are missing.
[46] *Cal. Stat. Pap. Dom. Add.*, 1660–70.

to have come of it and we may be certain that the expense would have been too great.

Morland did, however, help Lord Arlington with the gardens, for John Evelyn visited him there and records on 16 October 1671: 'The water furnishing the fountaines is raised by a pretty engine, on very slight plaine wheels, which likewise serve to grind his corne, from a small cascade of the canall, the invention of Sir Sam. Moreland.'

Speaking Trumpet: One of the early inventions of Morland was the speaking trumpet or 'Tuba Stentoro-phonica' as he grandiloquently named it. The horn or trumpet had been used, certainly from classical times, for giving signals and it is one of the earliest musical wind instruments. What led Morland to take up this subject we do not know, but he may have chanced upon a work by the Jesuit Athanasius Kircher (1601–80) who in 1643 published an account, from a MS. he found in the Vatican Library, of a horn by which Alexander the Great[47] could assemble his army at a distance of one hundred stadia (say 12 English miles). There is no evidence that this was done by speaking *through* the horn, yet the inference might have been drawn by Morland, assuming that he had seen Kircher's book, that it was feasible to do so.[48]

Morland designed and made several trumpets of different shapes and materials; in 1671 he wrote an account of the experiments he had made with them (see Bibliography Appendix II). He says: 'The first Instrument of this kind (though the invention had been long before digested in my thoughts) was made in glass in 1670.' It was about 32 in. long, 11 in. diam. at the large end and $2\frac{1}{2}$ in. at the small end.

[47] *Ars. Magna Lucis et Umbra,* 1643 fol. p. 102. 2nd. Ed. 1671.

[48] The history of the speaking trumpet and the claim on the behalf of Kircher to have invented it had been investigated by Beckmann, *History of Inventions,* Bohn's Ed. 1846, I, p. 98, with a great wealth of detail; the author has adopted his conclusion that Morland was the true inventor.

With this trumpet Morland was heard speaking a considerable distance. He then made another in brass about $4\frac{1}{2}$ ft. long, the large end 12 in. diam. and the small end $2\frac{1}{2}$ in.; the latter was shaped into a mouthpiece. 'Of this second Instrument, there were two trials taken very successfully in *St. James's Park;* where, at one time, the Lord *Angier,* standing by the Park-wall nearing *Goring House* heard me speaking (and that very distinctly) from the end of the Mall near *Old Spring Garden:* And at another time, His Majesty, His Royal Highness Prince *Rupert,* and divers of the Nobility and Gentry, standing at the end of the Mall near *Old Spring Garden,* heard me speaking (word for word) from the other end of the Mall (though the wind were contrary); which is 850 Yards or near $\frac{1}{2}$ of a measured *English* mile.'

Encouraged by the King, Morland made a third instrument of copper in the form of a trumpet, i.e. convoluted on itself, 16 ft. 8 in. total length, 19 in. diam. at the large end and 2 in. diam. at the small end. He carried this below London Bridge to Cuckolds Point and, leaving it in the hands of a waterman, rowed down to near Deptford; there, in despite of the noise going on around, he heard the waterman distinctly, the distance being judged to be $1\frac{1}{2}$ miles. He then made a fourth instrument of copper, again convoluted, 21 ft. long, 2 ft. diam. at the large end and $2\frac{1}{4}$ in. diam. at the small end, similar to the preceding, but better made. He then made a fifth instrument, about $5\frac{1}{2}$ ft. long, 21 in. diam. at the large end and 2 in. diam. at the small end; also two smaller instruments, dimensions $5\frac{1}{2}$ ft. $10\frac{1}{2}$ in. and $1\frac{1}{6}$ in. The third and fourth were heard from 'over against *Faux-Hall,* to the nearest part of *Battersey* over against *Chelsey;* And at another from *Hide-Park-Gate* to *Chelsey-Colledge'* say $1\frac{1}{2}$ miles. With the latter two he judged that a conversation could be maintained at a distance of three-quarters of a mile.

After that, the largest three were sent by His Majesty's command to Deal Castle to be tested. The Governor, Francis Digby, reported on 14 October 1671, that speech was heard distinctly at Walmer Castle, say 1 mile distant. The largest instrument was tried successfully between the shore and the ships riding at anchor, say two or three miles out. The report concludes, 'they will be of great use in all occasions where it's necessary to give Orders or Intelligence at a distance; but most of all at Sea.' Morland goes on to enumerate six advantages of the instrument on land and four at sea, but it is unnecessary to recite them here.

As showing Charles's sound judgment, Morland goes on to say, 'He has already given order for some of these Instruments of the smaller size (as judging them most useful) to be made and put into several of His Royal Ships and it is to be believed, that when the use of them shall be more publicly known, few Ships (whether Men of War or Merchant-men) will go to Sea without them.'

Morland made arrangements for supplying trumpets to the public, for on the title page of the above-mentioned work it is stated, 'the Instruments (or Speaking-trumpets) of all Sizes and Dimensions are Made and Sold by Mr. Simon Beal one of His Majesties Trump[eteer]s in Suffolk-street.'

In a review of Morland's book on this subject, the opinion was expressed that the best shape and dimensions 'must be settled by Experience rather than [by] Demonstrations'[49] because so many factors have to be taken into account. Morland was probably fully alive to this and would have perfected the trumpet, but it was for other reasons that he gave up the research. He says,[50] 'Had I not received some Discouragment (which then I did not think I deserved) I did not doubt but to have improved it to the distance of

[49] *Phil. Trans.*, Vol. VI, 1671, p. 3056.
[50] *Urim of Conscience*, p. 25. See Bibliography, appendix II.

eight, nine or ten miles.' How typical of the fate of inventions when first introduced! We can say, however, that the speaking trumpet gradually came into use from this time onwards and has proved a great boon especially to mariners.

One of Morland's speaking trumpets, perhaps made by Beale, is preserved in the Library of Trinity College, Cambridge. It was presented to the College by Thomas Boteler or Butler, who was made a Fellow in 1664 and died in 1708. It is straight like a coach horn, 6½ ft. long and 14¾ in. diam. at the orifice (see Plate V).

John Conyers in 1682 re-designed the instrument, 'having some years since try'd to make one of Sir S. Morland's trumpets', by making the receiving part of hyperboloidal form into the focus of which was placed the listening tube.[51] He got improved results because he was able to eliminate local sounds.

The speaking trumpet excited general interest at the time and must have become common knowledge, for we find Samuel Butler putting these words into the mouth of *Hudibras*, 1668:

> 'I heard a formidable voice
> Loud as the Stentorphonic noise.'

Morland made other experiments in acoustics and gives this account of them in the book mentioned above: 'I did likewise, at the same time, contrive and cause to be made by my Directions a very large *Otacousticon*, one end being laid to my Ear in a still evening, in the middle of *St. James's Park* brought into it (as I thought) innumerable Sounds of Coach and Cart-wheels, and humane Voices, in, and throughout all the streets as well those of *Westminster*, St. *James's* and *Pickadilly*, as the other between *White-hall* and *London*

---

[51] *Phil. Trans.*, XII, p. 1027.

Bridge.' He admits that his results were inconclusive and on account of the great weight and large dimensions of such instruments he 'then desisted from making any further experiments'.

A smaller form of the instrument was exhibited by Robert Hooke at a meeting of the Royal Society, but he does not say it was attributable to Morland. Here Pepys saw it and thus describes it:

2 April 1668: 'Here to my great content I did try the use of the Otacousticon which was only a great glass bottle broke at the bottom, putting the neck to my eare, and there I did plainly hear the dancing of the oares of the boats in the Thames to Arundel gallery window, which, without it, I could not in the least do, and may, I believe, be improved to a great height which I am mighty glad of.' We are to remember that the Royal Society then met at Gresham College in the City of London, so that Pepys heard the sound at a distance of about a couple of miles. He does not associate Morland's name with the instrument, but we assume it was one and the same apparatus. Consequently this fixes the date of its invention and incidentally that of the speaking trumpet and shows how long the ideas about them had been gestating in his thoughts. That Morland caught the public eye can be seen from the fact that it got into the theatre:

> *Ronca:* Sir, this is called an autocousticon.
> *Pandolfo:* Autocousticon! Why 'tis a pair of ass's ears, and large ones.
>
> *Albumazar*, i.3.

The attentive reader will see in these inventions the germs of the sound rangers and sound locators developed to such a high pitch of accuracy during the Great War, 1914–18, and subsequently.

Printing Press: Morland had something to do with the

establishment of a private printing press for the King, but what its nature was we do not know. It is unlikely that anything would transpire as to the use that was made of it but it suggests that Morland was still working behind the scenes. There is reference to 'keeping the King's private printing press'[52] in 1672 and we couple this with a 'Warrant to Samuel Morland to erect a private printing press within the Court for the use of[53] the Government.' We have found no further reference to it, which is perhaps not to be wondered at.

Capstans:

'Sir Samuel Morland hath now another fancy concerning weighing anchors,' so the King wrote to Prince Rupert 6 August 1673.[54] On 4 June of the following year Sir Robert Moray, who was in close touch with the Court, brought to the notice of the Royal Society Morland's proposal of a method of weighing anchors with ease and safety. Hooke, as usual, not to be out-faced, affirmed that several years earlier he had invented a convenient method of doing the same thing. Morland's 'fancy,' so far as we can make out, was merely the provision of a click or pawl engaging with a locked ring on the capstan at deck level so as to prevent the anchor taking charge, overcoming the seamen working the capstan bars, and probably injuring them.

Stoves:

Morland seems to have had something to do with stoves for burning fuel in confined situations, such as on board ship. In 1667, 26 March, a warrant was issued for a patent

[52] *Cal. Treas. Books*, 1672–75 p. 143.
[53] *Cal. Stat. Pap. Dom.*, Charles II, 1673, Aug. 2.
[54] Brit. Mus. Lansdown MS. 1236, fol. 170, quoted in Bryant *Letters of King Charles II*.

for 14 years in favour of Col. Thomas Culpeper 'for making iron hearths of his own invention for burning coals, instead of the freestone hearths which are liable to crack.' There is a minute to the effect that an after-draft of this grant was made to Sir Sam. Morland, Bart., Rich. Wigmore, Rob. Lindsey and the aforesaid Culpeper.[55] The actual patent was dated 13 January 1668 (No. 151) and the grant was to the aforesaid for 'a new and perfect Invencon of hearths of cast iron, brasse or copper which will not only be durable, but usefull in all kinds of Chimneys and for all sortes of fuell, and very much prevent the great expense thereof.' There is no specification and no drawing as one would expect. In the author's opinion, Morland cannot have been the inventor; rather he was associated in the grant, as was quite usual at that time, because it was believed that he could, through his influence at Court, facilitate the grant and smooth its passage through the various offices. It would appear also that the invention did not come into use, for nine years later in 1676 a patent (No. 197) was granted to William Castle and Henry Ewbank, for a like invention, which we find advertised in the *London Gazette* 4–7 September 1676 in these words: ' . . . fire hearths for ships made of iron, copper and other mettal.' Col. Ewbanks's 'new fashioned firehearths were approved for the Royal Navy on 16 December 1676,[56] and they were ordered to be set up in the new galley frigates.' From that date we may conclude that such iron stoves became common on shipboard. These stoves were, as may be imagined, a boon against risk of fire where brick flues could not be built, but there could not be much that was patentable in them. However, the word 'patent' has always been an asset when manufacturing and marketing a convenient design.

[55] *Cal. Stat. Pap. Dom.*, 230, No. 66, Entry Book 25, p. 2.
[56] Tanner, J. R., *Catalogue of Pepysian MSS.*, iv., 385.

Barometer:

The discovery of the fact that the atmosphere has pressure and Torricelli's invention of a method for measuring it by means of the mercurial barometer in 1644, were events of such outstanding importance that the whole scientific world was interested and repercussions took place in every country. Pascal with great insight reasoned, and by actual trial demonstrated, that the pressure of the atmosphere diminished as one ascended a mountain. Many men—De la Hire, Christiaan Huyghens and Hooke, 1668, set to work to experiment with the barometer and invent improvements or adaptations. The situation is strikingly described by Roger North, who also tells us how Morland took a hand in the affair.[57] He says that 'about this time, the philosophical world was entertained about settling the grand affair of the mercurial barometer and its indications. Among the rest, Sir Samuel Moreland published a piece containing a device to prolong the indicatory space from three inches, as in common tubes, to a foot, or more as you please; and he defied all the virtuosi to resolve it. This he called the statick barometer.' We have not been able to trace the publication referred to, but North proceeds to give a long description of the apparatus, the essence of which is as follows. The barometer tube is suspended from one arm of a balance beam and counterpoised by a weight on the other arm, which is furthermore provided with an index working over a graduated open scale corresponding to inches of mercury. The lower end of the barometer tube is immersed as usual in a cistern of mercury about twice the diameter of the tube. The rising and falling of the mercury in the tube causes the latter to fall or rise and transmit movement to the scale. 'His lordship wrote a paper in answer to the knight's

[57] *Life of the Rt. Hon. Francis North, Baron Guilford*, New Edn. 1826, Vol. II, p. 197.

challenge . . . and concluded that the mystery lay in the difference of specific gravity between mercury and glass, which may be nearly as one to twenty.' The total range of the mercury under atmospheric pressure, being roughly three inches, the loss or gain of immersion of the glass tube must balance possibly a quarter of an inch of mercury and as the action that takes place is not amenable to calculation the scale must be graduated by calibration. In practice it was found that the friction of the mercury in the tube and that of the tube in the cistern were sufficient to vitiate the readings and the barometer was 'not made use of but for show.'

'When the virtuoso received his lordship's paper he blustered and threatened the most powerful answer, but never was so kind as to send any. On the contrary, he took an opportunity to wait on his lordship and they became good philosophical friends and acquaintance.' Another design by Morland for a barometer is figured by Desaguliers:[58] the upper part of the barometer tube is bent at an angle so that the apparent rise and fall of the mercury is thereby multiplied and thus makes the reading more open than it is in a vertical tube. The meniscus is distorted so that doubt arises in reading it, besides which the added friction of the mercury in the glass tube causes sluggishness. Desaguliers's criticism that 'this Contrivance is more ingenious than happy, and that one may almost as soon trust a common Barometer,' is one with which the author quite concurs. He has not come across an existing example of either of these kinds of barometers, which is contemporary with Morland.

The date of Morland's apparatus is fixed by these entries by Hooke in his *Diary*:
'24 December 1677—He (the King) told me of Sir S. Moreland's weather glasse and bid me make one for him.
2 February 1678—Win about Sir S. Moreland barometer

[58] *Experimental Philosophy*, II, 1743, p. 262, pl. XXI. fig. i.

7 August—He (Wren) told me of Sir Sam Moorland's barometer'.

We do not imagine that Hooke devoted much time to the task demanded by the King because, as usual with him, he was satisfied he could go one better with apparatus of his own, and that was the wheel barometer—the forerunner of the barometers we see quite commonly today.

Since the foregoing was written Dr. W. E. Knowles Middleton has found a much earlier attribution than Desaguliers's, of the inclined tube barometer to Morland.[59] In 1688 a London clockmaker, John Smith, wrote a six-penny pamphlet about the barometer in which the following passage occurs:[60]

'Baroscopes have heretofore been made up after divers manners, but chiefly three ways: As first, that now commonly used, with a streight tube, ascribed chiefly to the noble Boyle. Secondly, that with a tube, whose top inclines, devised by Sir Samuel Morland. Thirdly, the wheel-baroscope, invented by the ingenious Mr. Robert Hook (and described in his Micography[sic]) but of these three sorts, the two last are but seldom used, by reason of some inconveniences either in the shape or charge; Sir Samuel's being such as will not admit of any regular figure, and Mr. Hooks being very dear and costly'. (See note on page 55.)

Second Marriage

It was not long after the death of his first wife, in fact after a widowerhood of less than two years, that Morland married again. His choice fell upon Carola, a girl of only nineteen years of age, daughter of Sir Roger Harsnett, Sergeant-at-Arms to the House of Lords, and Carola his

[59] Knowles Middleton, W. E., *The History of the Barometer*, Baltimore, 1963, p. 110.
[60] Smith, John, *A Compleat Discourse of the Nature, Use and Right Managing of that Wonderful Instrument the Baroscope or Quicksilver Weather Glass*, London, 1688, p. 1.

E

wife. The marriage took place on 26 October 1670, in Westminster Abbey, and not at St. Margaret's, Westminster, the Parish Church, as one might reasonably have expected. This suggests to us a desire for ostentation on the part either of Morland or of the Harsnett family. There were two children of the marriage—the first a daughter, Thynne, born sometime about August 1671, who died in December of that year and was buried in the Cloisters 19 December 1671. The second child, named Edward, born, as the following inscription states, on 4 October 1674, was baptised on 16 October at St. Margaret's, Westminster. The child survived till June 1675, when he was buried in the Cloisters on the 11th of that month; his name, by the way, is entered in the Burial Register as Edmond.[61] Carola, however, died in childbed on 10 October 1674, and was buried in the Abbey on the 14th of that month.

The sad story is revealed by a monumental inscription in the South Aisle which reads as follows:

CAROLA
DAVGHTER OF ROGER HARSNETT ESQ:
AND OF CAROLA HIS WIFE
YE TRVLY LOVING (& AS TRVLY BELOVED)
WIFE OF SAMVEL MORLAND KT. & BART.
BARE A SECOND SON OCTOB. 4TH
DIED OCTOBER 10TH
ANNO DOMINI 1674
AETATIS. XXIII°

This is preceded by two inscriptions laudatory of the deceased, one in Hebrew and one in Greek, the translations of which are as follows:

[61] This information is extracted from Chester, J. L., *Westminster Abbey Registers*, 1876.

Hebrew: Blessed be Thou of the Lord, my honoured
Wife! Thy memory shall be a blessing, O
virtuous Woman.

Greek: When I think of thy mildness, patience, charity,
modesty, and piety, I lament thee, O most
excellent creature! and grieve exceedingly: but
not like those who have no hope; for I believe
and expect the resurrection of them that sleep in
Christ.[62]

The arms of Morland dimidiated with those of his wife are
sculptured and painted on the monument. Those of Morland
are: Sable in chief a lion passant guardant, in base a leopard's
head jessant à fleur de lis, all or, an escutcheon of the bloody
hand.

Third Marriage

Only two years after the death of his second wife, Morland married for the third time, and again his choice fell
upon a mere girl, younger even—for she was only sixteen—
than his previous wife, in the person of Ann, third daughter
of George Filding or Feilding and Mary his wife of Solihull
co. Warwick. The marriage took place in Westminster
Abbey, instead of at Solihull as would naturally be expected,
on 16 November 1676, and this time we can only conclude
that it was Morland himself who wanted to make a display.
What his acquaintances thought about the marriage is
shown in a letter dated 30 November 1676, from Sir John
Verney to Sir Ralph Verney:[63] 'Sir Samuel Morland is
lately married to handsome Fielding's sister, and saith he
will not have a penny for portion. She is handsomer for a
woman than he is for a man.' Once more the marriage was

[62] Neale, J. P., *History and antiquities of the Abbey Church of St. Peter, Westminster,*
II, 1823, p. 238.

[63] *Hist. MSS. Comn.,* V, 467b, Verney MSS.

short-lived—little over three years—for Ann died on 20 February 1680, and was buried in the Abbey four days later. We do not learn whether there were any children of this marriage. The event is recorded in the Abbey on a monument close to the preceding one in these words:

ANN
Daughter of GEORGE FILDING Esq:
and of MARY his wife
the truly loving (& as truly beloved)
Wife of
SAMVEL MORLAND Kt. & Bartt.
died February 20th
Anno Domini. $167\frac{9}{80}$
Aetatis XIX°

As on the previous monument, this inscription is preceded by others in foreign languages; in this case one is in Hebrew followed by one in Coptic, the translations of which are as follows:

Hebrew: O thou fairest among women! Thou virtuous woman! The hand of the Lord hath done this. The Lord gave and the Lord hath taken away!— Blessed be the name of the Lord.

Coptic: Come, let us weep with an honoured husband for thee; hoping that thou art departed in Christ. This lady was truly religious, sincere and chaste while she lived.—Praised and blessed was she in her death.

As before, Morland's coat of arms is dimidiated with that of his wife. We are inclined to think that Morland was not so much concerned to lavish panegyrics on his wives as to take the opportunity to show off his knowledge of foreign languages. Both these monuments, made by the same stone-mason Stanton, are so much alike in size, style with Ionic columns at the sides and shield of arms above, in presentation and symmetry of position that one is tempted to think that they were put up at the same time. Perhaps he was flush of money at the time, as the pumps and fire engines may have been bringing in an income.

These two monuments are those referred to by Addison in the *Spectator* 30 March 1711, where he states that when in serious humour he often walked by himself in Westminster Abbey: 'this great Magazine of Mortality,' he examined the monuments and observed that 'some of them were covered with such extravagant Epitaphs, that if it were possible for the dead Person to be acquainted with them, he would blush at the Praises which his Friends have bestowed upon him. There are others so excessively modest, that they deliver the Character of the Person departed in *Greek* or *Hebrew*, and by that means are not understood once in a Twelve-month.'

It was, perhaps, in anticipation of this third marriage that Morland in 1675 took a lease for thirty-one years from the Duchy of Cornwall of Vauxhall House in the Manor of Kennington; this was the house on the site of the Ordnance Factory established by Charles I;[64] from the original warrant 4 December 1674, it appears that the property was then held in trust for the relations of Kaspar Kalthoff, who had been the trusted mechanic of the Marquis of Worcester from 1629–67, and had been employed there on the Marquis's inventions. We can hardly resist the surmise that Morland had got to know of this and thought that the workshop there, though no longer used as such, might be reconditioned and be useful to him. A fortnight later than the date given, Morland received a grant of £400 to buy out

[64] *Trans. Newc. Soc.*, XIII, 75, *'Marquis of Worcester and Vauxhall'*, by Thorpe, W. H.

the interest of the relatives and presumably a new lease was arranged lasting till 1705.

The situation was then countrified, yet handy to the Court, for it was but a short coach journey over Westminster Bridge. The house was next door to Vauxhall Armoury where the Marquis of Worcester had experimented with his steam engine in 1666, and this fact may have some significance, for trained artificers were probably still there.

Here Morland, giving rein to his mechanical instinct experimented with his pumps and his steam engine and fitted up quite a number of devices. John Evelyn alludes to this on the occasion of a visit he paid on 15 September 1681 'to see his house and mechanicks.' An excellent account[65] of them is given by Roger North who says that 'His Lordship did not often dine from his own house; and when he did, it was commonly at a particular virtuoso's, as with Sir Peter Lely, Mr. Hugh May, Sir Samuel Moreland or the like.' On one of these occasions, 'though his entertainment was exquisite, the greatest pleasure was to observe his devices; for everything showed art and mechanism. A large fountain played in the room and all the glasses stood under little streams of water. He had a cistern in his garret which supplied water to all parts of his house, as he thought fit to contrive it. The water was raised by a common pump (as it seemed to be) in his yard, but, going to lift the sweep, it rose (as it were) of itself; for it was prolonged beyond the tree and there had a counterpoise of lead; which made the sweep move as the beam of a scale; and wherever there was likely to be friction, a roulet was placed to receive it. In like manner, windows, doors, hinges, and chimnies, spoke the owner to be an artist: and his utensils abroad had the same taste. His coach was most particular; and he made a portable

[65] *The Life of the Rt. Hon. Francis North, Lord Guilford, Lord Keeper of the Great Seal of England*, ed. A. Jessop, 1826, Vol. I, p. 312, Vol. II, p. 197.

engine that moved by watchwork, which might be called a kitchen; for it had a fire-place and grate, with which he could make a soup, broil costeletts or roast an egg; and for that his contrivance was by a fork with fine tines (as I may call it) which stood upright at a due distance before the firegrate and turned slowly. An egg, put into that, would roast according to art; and if a piece of meat were stuck upon it, it was dressed by clockwork. He said himself that this machine cost him 30 *l.* He took it with him in his own coach and, at inns, he was his own cook.'

In 1679, Morland published his '*Doctrine of Interest both simple and compound*' as already mentioned, on page 34.

Note on the Invention of the Inclined Tube Barometer.

Since this Chapter was set in type, the Editors' attention has been drawn to a further discovery by Dr. W. E. Knowles Middleton. An instrument, which was in effect an inclined tube barometer, is described in a copy of a letter written apparently in 1657 by Paolo del Buono (1625–1659).

See W. E. K. Middleton, *Paolo del Buono on the Elasticity of Air.* Archive for History of Exact Science, Vol. 6, No. 1, p. 1. Springer-Verlag, Berlin, 1969.

CHAPTER IV

PUMPS AND PUMPING PLANT
1675–81

Pumps for the Navy; Isaac Thompson contracts to make his pumps; Pumps at Windsor Castle; Created 'Master of Mechanicks', Fourth Marriage

Of all the directions in which Morland exercised his inventive talent, none was more fruitful than that of pumps and pumping. As has already been stated, this problem of raising water for domestic and industrial purposes had by the seventeenth century become urgent, and many were the attempts, as the Patent Rolls of the period show, to improve or amplify existing means or to devise entirely new ones. Hitherto, however, they had not met with any striking success. Before enlarging on what Morland did, it is well to understand the types of pumps commonly in use when he came upon the scene. Excluding low-lift primitive devices which were obsolescent, there were three types: the rag-and-chain pump; the suction pump and the combination with it of a lifting pump; and the piston or plunger pump. It is hardly necessary to remark that all of them are still in use. The first, as its name implies, consisted of balls, discs or packed material strung together with links into an endless chain, dipping into the water below, drawn upwards through a pipe on one side over a pulley and hanging free on the other side; the motive power was usually animal. Examples of this kind of pump were used in mines, and lifts of as much as 240 ft. depth were attained with it.

The suction pump had a piston or bucket packed with leather, reciprocating in a barrel, generally of wood but sometimes of brass or copper. In the bucket were holes covered with leather flap-valves; the pressure of the atmosphere, which is equivalent to that of a column of water, 32 ft. high, caused the water to follow the bucket to something approaching this height. A foot-valve prevented the water falling back, and on the return stroke the water passed through the bucket, so that on the next upstroke the water lying on the bucket could be lifted to any reasonable height.

In the third type of pump a 'forcer', i.e. a long piston or plunger covered with leather, reciprocated in a barrel, usually of brass, perhaps six or seven in. diam., that being the diameter within the capacity of gun-boring machines of the period. It was this type which was used in bridge waterworks, such as that at London Bridge, where undershot waterwheels were placed in the landward arches of the bridge and actuated by the head of water flowing through. The power of the wheel was transmitted to the pumps by such mechanism as a crank and rocking beam. The height of the lift was limited only by the power of the wheels and the materials used in the construction of the pipes to about 200 ft.

It was upon this latter field of service that Morland entered. He had the brilliant idea of providing a leather collar in the neck of the pump barrel instead of packing the plunger and making the latter, carefully turned in a lathe, work through this packing; in other words, he transferred the packing from the plunger to the barrel, thereby obviating the difficult task, with the means then available, of boring a cylinder truly, and only had the much simpler task of turning the plunger. His pump needed greater refinement in its construction and more extended use of metals than in the case of the bucket pump but the state of the mechanic arts at this time was equal to the fresh demands upon it. Morland recognised this, and has a further claim on our remembrance because he took steps, as we shall see later, to have his pump produced on a commercial scale.

The idea of the collar packing occurred to Morland about 1665, if we are to accept the statement made just before his death that he had spent forty years in studying means for raising water. In another statement made in 1677 he said that his invention was the result of twenty years study and the expenditure of thousands of pounds. The second statement tallies fairly well with the one above, while the statement as to the money he had expended, though possibly exaggerated, is supported by the fact that he had been at the expense of setting up one of his engines at Woolwich Dockyard. There on 10 September 1673, the King, attended by the principal officers of the Navy and many of his courtiers, saw the pump in action, working more efficiently than the chain pump or others then in use. This is the report that appeared in the press:[66]

'Whitehal, Sept. 12. Upon Wednesday the tenth instant, His Majesty, attended by the Principal Officers of the Navy and divers other Persons of Quality, went down to Wolwich, to see the working of two Water-Engines, Contrived and Invented by Sir Samuel Morland, who of late years has not unsuccessfully applyed his Studies to things of Practice and publick Use; And His Majesty was so well satisfied of their usefulness (one Man performing more by these Engines, than eight Men are able to do by any chain Pump, or other Engine yet in Use, besides that they are of a small Charge, and not easy to be put out of Order in many years) that he has Ordered one of these Engines to be carried to Chatham, to empty and clean that Dock of Water, which no Engineer or Artist could ever yet do effectually, as a thing

[66] *London Gazette*, 11–15 September 1673.

which will be of no small advantage to his Shipping and Service, and intends also that some of these new Pumps shall be put up in all his Ships, great and small, and the Chain Pump and other hand Pumps now in use, to be wholly laid aside, as probably they may likewise be at Land, these new Pumps being alike useful for Mines, Brewhouses, Wells, and all private Families whatsoever.'

The King, with his usual perspicacity, saw its advantages to shipping and, as stated above, gave instructions that one of the pumps was to be set up at Chatham for trial, intending that other types of pump should eventually be discarded. The outcome of the visit is recorded in an Admiralty letter to the Navy Board on 24 September 1673.[67] 'Whereas Sir Samuel Morland has set up an engine at Woolwich for the raising and delivering of great quantities of water with a less proportion of strength than hath hitherto been practised' and has undertaken to transport it to Chatham, where by wind 'or the easy labour of an horse when at any time the wind shall fail' it may 'clear that dock of the water with which it is continually annoyed' and may remain in a constant condition of service and repair for seven years. The Board to make out a bill to Morland for £350.

After further correspondence, on 2 December 1673 Pepys informed the Navy Board that the materials for the engine Morland is setting up for the King at Chatham are now ready for dispatch. What the outcome was we do not learn, but we infer that the pump was not quite equal to the duties that had been expected from it, for the business dragged on till 1676. Pepys, writing to the Navy Board on 16 November of that year,[68] arranged to go down to Chatham with the Surveyor of the Navy for a final trial and on the 20 April he

[67] Tanner, J. R., *Navy Records Society*, 'Naval MSS. in the Pepysian Library at Magdalene College, Cambridge,' 1926, II, 66, et seq.
[68] *Loc. cit.*, III, 323, 329, 407.

is directed by the King to instruct the officers of the Yard at Deptford to take out one of the chain pumps from the 'Jersey' frigate in order that Morland may make an experiment with a pump of his in place of it. By this we judge that the pump had now come down to the less ambitious task of pumping bilge water from a vessel, than that of emptying the Dock.

During this time Morland had been very busy and had lost no time in applying for some reward for his invention. In the first place he petitioned Parliament for an Act for the protection of his invention. The course of the Bill through the Commons will be gathered from the following extracts:[69]

29 January 1673/4. 'A petition of Sir Samuell Mooreland for leave to bring in a Bill for the Use of a certain Water Engine, by him invented, was read. Resolved, that it be referred to Sir Robert Howard (and other names given) and such other of the Members as will accompany them, or any five of them to repair to take a view of the said Engine, and report their opinions thereon to the House, on Monday next.'

12 February 1673/4. 'A Bill to enable Sir Samuell Moreland to enjoy the whole benefit of certain Pumps by him invented was read a First time resolved, etc. that this Bill be read a Second Time.'

24 February 1673/4. 'Sir John Mallet reports from the Com'tee to whom Sir Samuel Moreland's Bill was committed, several Amendments, agreed by the Com'tee to be made to the Bill: which he read in his place; afterwards delivered the same in at the Clerk's Table: where they were once read: and the Amendments to the Claim marked (B) being read a Second Time, were, with some Amendments made at the Table, upon the Question, severally agreed unto.'

[69] *Journal of the House of Commons*, Vol. 9, pp. 300, 308, 314.

Parliament was prorogued on the date last named and we conclude that Morland decided, rather than wait till the next session, when the whole procedure would have to be gone through afresh, to apply for the possibly less valuable privilege of Letters Patent. This was granted on 14 March (No. 175) to 'Sr. Samuell Morland' for 'severall engines for raising great quantities of water with farr less p'porcon of strength than can be p'formed either by chaine pump or other engine now in use.' Meanwhile Morland sought publicity for his invention for, after showing it to the King at the Banqueting House in Whitehall on 16 February, on the 23rd he exhibited it to the Lord Mayor and Aldermen of the City of London at Grocers' Hall. Hooke recorded in his *Diary* that he and a friend saw it there on 8 May 1674. That there were three of Morland's engines at Grocers' Hall on 4 September 1674 is shown by the following recently discovered letter, which he addressed to Sir Robert Clayton on that date.[70]

'The 3 Engins ye Duke bespoke are all finish't & lodg'd in Grossers Hall with May[r]. Hassenett & are as good as I can possibly make them. And for ye price I shall abate ten pounds of ye 2 fire Engines of what I askt in case ye Duke take them as they are without cases, but if I may case them, all up, I cannot abate above eight. So that I received 65, and if they bee sent away as they are, I shall receive but fifty five pound more. And if cased up fifty seven. And I entreat you to pay ye Money to May[r]. Hassenett, who has an Acquittance signed by yr. most humble st.
4 Sept 1674

For his honored freind   S. Morland
   S[r] Rob[t] Clayton

---

[70] Lambeth Palace Library, MS. 2165, f. 24, 25.

[Added in   The great engin — 60
left margin]   ye 2 other 30^1 apiece — 60
                120
I have a very neat fire engin
in hand for yourself, wch will
be finisht in 8 days.'

It is clear that Morland could not have carried out the exhibition before the King and the public demonstration
without having at his back, besides financial support, some
effective and skilled help in constructing and operating
the pump. Such was the case; his chief coadjutor was one
Isaack Thompson 'Engin-Maker living in Great Russel-
Street, near Southampton-House, at the Sign of Sir Samuel
Morland's Fire-Engin.' We learn this from a SCHEDULE
printed on a single sheet[71], undated but from the reference
in it to the exhibition at Grocers' Hall, issued in 1675. This
Schedule is of exceptional interest and deserves close
study (see Fig. 1). The document opens with the statement
that Morland had made a final agreement with his workmen
concerning his new pumps and water-engines. It is in fact a
price list and as such is in all probability the earliest printed
engineering price list extant. It will be observed that Morland offered his pumps in a variety of types: for private
houses; for mines or deep wells; for ships of all rates; for
emptying ponds and for draining low grounds; and lastly,
for extinguishing fires. All of these were made in different
sizes: the plungers ranged from 3 in. to 10 in. diam. Models
of most of these engines were to be seen fixed and working
in Thompson's yard. Details of construction and material
are given of both bucket and plunger pumps. The proviso,
that an extra charge for erection beyond twenty miles from
London would be made, shows that the Schedule had been
well thought out. The approximate site of this seventeenth

[71] *Brit. Mus.*, B. 16. No. 10 (90–91).

century engineering shop is of some interest. Southampton, later Russell, House occupied the northern side of what is now Bloomsbury Square. Thompson's workshop was further west and we should fix it to have been opposite the eastern end of the site now occupied by the British Museum.

Morland had some kind of a contract with Thompson, as is indicated by the latter's 'Advertisement' (see Fig. 2). The date is unfortunately lacking and that ascribed to it is conjectural. What exactly were the terms of the contract and its duration we are unable to say. The advertisement gives no information additional to that on the 'Schedule' except that Thompson's street sign is now simply 'The Engine' instead of 'Sir Samuel Morland's Fire Engin.'

It is not difficult to imagine that the King, after seeing the trials described above, should visualise the possibilities of improving the water supplies of the Royal residences and should decide to instal the pump at Windsor Castle. There had been a domestic supply there as early as the middle of the sixteenth century; this was the time when gravitation water supplies to cities and large communities had become general, witness Wolsey's supply to Hampton Court. In 1610 Abraham Greene, 'His Majesty's sergeant plumber', was paid 'for lead, brass, solder, workmanship and repairing of the conduit pipes and heads in the Forest of Windsor, and the fountain in the Castle of Windsor, for the better passage of water to the said Castle £650.10s.'[72]

The King realised that water could now be raised from ground level to such an elevation as would command a supply at any desired point in the new buildings now being erected there, and Morland duly installed the pump.

It may be that this encouraged Morland to pursue his attempt to secure the Act of Parliament which had been so summarily cut short by the prorogation of the last session.

[72] Devon, *Issues of the Exchequer.*

Sir SAMUEL MORLAND

Having made a final Agreement with his WORKMEN, concerning his New *PUMPS* and *WATER-ENGINS*, and having brought them to as low Rates as they can be afforded, has thought fit, for the better satisfaction of all Persons concerned, to Publish the following *Schedule*.

A SCHEDULE

CONTAINING

The several Rates or Prizes that Sir *SAMUEL MORLAND*'s New Pumps or Water-Engins are to be sold for, according to their several and respective Dimensions.

1. PUMPS for private Houses.

I. For a *Pump* with an Iron frame and Fly, with two Leaden Weights of about Thirty pound, The Bucket and Neck of Brass, the Head and Pipe of about two Foot in Length made of Lead, the Diameter of the Bucket three Inches; and all fixed to a framed Stool, fit for that purpose — Five pound.

II. For a *Pump* of the same sort, the Diameter of the Bucket being three Inches and an half — Six pound.

III. For a *Pump* of the same sort, the Diameter of the Bucket being four Inches — Seven pound.

IV. For a *Pump* of the same sort, the Diameter of the Bucket being four Inches and an half — Nine pound.

V. For a *Pump* of the same sort, the Diameter of the Bucket being five Inches — Eleven pound.

VI. For a *Pump* of the same sort, the Diameter of the Bucket being five Inches and an half — Twelve pound.

VII. For a *Pump* of the same sort, the Diameter of the Bucket being six Inches — Fifteen pound.

VIII. For a *Pump* of the same sort, the Diameter of the Bucket being six Inches and an half — Seventeen pound.

IX. For a *Pump* of the same sort, the Diameter of the Bucket being seven Inches — Twenty pound.

X. For a *Pump* of the same sort, the Head and Pipe being of Brass, and the Diameter of the Bucket three Inches — Eight pound.

XI. For a Forcing *Pump* of Lead with two Valves, the Forcer three Inches Diameter — Nine pound.

XII. For such a Forcing *Pump*, the Forcer being four Inches Diameter — Thirteen pound.

XIII. For such a Forcing *Pump* of Lead to Force Water out of a Well fifty or sixty Foot Deep, to be made in all the parts of it, like to the *Engin* set, part on the top, and part in the Well, at *Windsor* Castle, the Iron-Rods and all things, excepting the Leaden Pipes — Twenty six pound.

2. ENGINS for Mines or deep Wells.

XIV. For such a Brass *Forcing-Engin*, as Forced up the Water to the top of the Tower at *Greews-Hall*, with eight Flyes, and Fourscore Foot of Leaden Pipe to it of two Inches Diameter, and the Forcer three Inches, three Inches and an half or four Inches Diameter — Sixty pound.

XV. For such an *Engin*, being divided into two parts, the one to be placed at the bottom of a *Well*, or *Pit*, and the other at the top, with Fourscore Foot of Leaden Pipe, of two Inches Diameter, and an Iron Rod, and five Brass Valves, with double Bridges, and all things, else fit for use to it, and letting up and fixing them within Twenty Miles of *London*. [If further, the Workman must be paid for his journey and labour over and above.] — Sixty one pound ten shillings.

XVI. For the same *Engin*, with fourscore Foot of Leaden Pipe, and five Brass Valves with double Bridges, standing at a distance from a *Well* or *Pit*, [besides the additional Fourscore Foot of Leaden Pipe, and Rod, which is to be paid for over and above] — Sixty three pound ten shillings.

XVII. For either of these two *Engins*, without the Fourscore Foot of Leaden Pipe, and without three of the five Brass Valves — Forty six pound.

XVIII. For a *Pump*, the Pipe whereof is of Wood, about twenty Foot long, with a *Pump* on the Head of it, consisting of two Iron Cheeks, a Crank, Four Flyes, a Brass Bucket of Four Inches Diameter, working in a Neck of Brass, together with an Iron Rod, and a Wooden Sucker at the bottom, fitted for use — Nine pound.

3. *ENGINS proper and useful for Ships of all Rates, as likewise for Emptying Ponds, or Draining Low Grounds.*

XIX. FOr a *Pump*, the Head whereof is a square Box of Wood, with two Iron Frames and a double Crank, at the top thereof drawing } **Twenty pound.**
the Water eight or ten Foot, and delivering about fourscore Tun an Hour, with the strength of three men

XX. For a *Pump* of the same kind, of excellent use for *Ships*, drawing Water from Ten to Twenty or Twenty four Foot, with the strength } **From Twenty to**
of one, two, or three men **Eight pounds.**

XXI. For a great *Wooden Engin*, with a Wheel of Wood and Flaps, turning in a Trough of Wood, which raises near Two Hundred } **fourteen pound.**
Tun an Hour, about four Foot high

XXII. And for such a Forcing *Pump* as was made for Alderman *Backwell*, with a Wooden Box six Inches within one way, and four } **five pound ten**
the other way **shillings.**

4. *ENGINS to quench Fire, or wet the Sails of Ships, such as were tryed before His Majesty near the Banquetting-House at White-hall, and compared with the White-hall Engins, upon Tuesday, the Sixteenth of February; And upon Tuesday, the Twenty third of February before the Right Honourable the Lord Mayor and the Worshipful the Aldermen of the City of London, and several other Persons of Quality at Grocers-hall, where were likewise brought, by the Lord Mayor's special Order, two of the best Engins of the City to be compared with them.*

XXIII. FOr a Fire Engin, with one Pair of Handles, the Forcer being five Inches Diameter ——————— } **Twenty three pound**
XXIV. For the same Engin, with two Pair of Handles ——————— } **Twenty six pound.**
XXV. For such an Engin, with a Forcer of six Inches Diameter ——————— } **Twenty nine pound.**
XXVI. For such an Engin, with a Forcer of eight Inches Diameter ——————— } **Thirty two pound.**
XXVII. For such an Engin, with a Forcer of ten Inches Diameter ——————— } **Forty eight pound.**

If Carriages be desired to any of these *Engins*, the Work-man must be paid for them over and above the aforesaid Prizes.

Any of these *Engins* are made by, and may be bespoke of, *Isaak Thompson*, Engin-Maker, living in Great *Russel-street* near *Southampton-House*, at the Sign of Sir *Samuel Morland*'s Fire-Engin, where any Person may see in his Yard exact Models of most of the aforesaid *Pumps* and *Engins* Fixed and Working.

Fig. 1.   Sir Samuel Morland's Schedule of prices of Pumps, 1675.   See page 62.

F

ADVERTISEMENT.

THESE are to give Notice: That the Articles between Sr SAMUEL MORELAND and ISAAC THOMPSON (Their Majesties sworn *Engine-Maker*) being expired; The said THOMPSON is now at Liberty to make any Engine for drawing up the *Thames* Water for the Service of *London* and *Westminster* or elsewhere: And that he makes all sorts of Pumps for Private Houses, for Mines or deep Wells, and Pumps proper and useful for Ships of all Rates, as likewise for emptying Ponds, or draining low Grounds; Engines to quench Fire, or wet Sails of Ships, such as were tried before His Majesty near the Banqueting House at *Whitehall*, and before the Right Honorable the Lord Mayor and the Worshipful the Aldermen of the City of *London*, and several other Persons of Quality at *Grocers-Hall*: And these, at cheaper Rates than formerly, sold. He also hath invented a Sucker for any Engine or Pump, which will not stick and faulture as others usually do, which was never done before.

Any of these Engines are made by ISAAC THOMPSON at the Sign of the *Engine* in Great *Russel-Street* overagainst *Montague House*: Where you may have all manner of *Plummers* Moulds for Casting of Pipes; and where any Person may see exact Models of the abovesaid Pumps and Engines fixed and working.

Fig. 2.   Isaac Thompson's Advertisement of Pumps, *c*. 1681. See page 63.

The course of the Bill through the Commons can be gathered by the following entries: '1676/7 20 March. A Bill for allowing Sir Samuel Moreland the Benefit of Pumps and Water Engines by him invented was read. Resolved: that the Bill be read a second time.' '1677 2 April. The Bill for allowing Sir Samuel Moreland the Benefit of Pumps and Water Engines, by him invented, was read the second time. Resolved: that the Bill be committed to Mr. Vaughan (and others named) and they are to summon and hear all parties concerned and to meet on Wednesday next, at two of the clock in the afternoon in the Exchequer Chamber and are impowered to send for Persons, Papers and Records.'[73]

The Bill met with considerable opposition from interested persons mainly, it would seem, from the lack of definition on the part of Morland of the privilege he wished to secure. It would be still fresh in the minds of some Members of the House that the Marquis of Worcester had secured, in 1663, an Act (15 Car. II cap. XII) for his 'Water-Commanding Engine', whatever that was, for 99 years and it would be realised that there was a danger of creating monopolies that would hamper the course of invention in this desirable sphere of activity. Since the passage of the Statute of Monopolies in 1607, Parliament had been alive to such a danger. Morland was constrained, therefore, to set out in detail what he sought to protect and did so in an 'Answer to several Papers and Persons against his Bill for the New Water-Engine.'[74] He stated that the principal parts of this engine were two in number, viz. '1. The playing of a brass bucket or forcer into a chamber of water through a narrow neck of brass in which is placed a small fillet of leather curiously prepared. 2. The reducing of the circular motion of a crank into a perpendicular motion within an iron frame between

[73] *Journ. Ho. of Commons*, Vol. IX, pp. 402, 412.
[74] *Brit. Mus.* 816 m. 10/93 and *Cal. Stat. Pap. Dom.* 1677.

two brass rollers.' He goes on to say that on his petition a
Bill for the sole use thereof would have passed the last
Session, had not Parliament been prorogued. He had set
up an engine at Windsor Castle in a well, which by the
labour of one man, raises 12 barrels an hour 140 feet;
and his invention is new, but he submits to the Committee
to strike out anything they please from his Bill. With a
certificate by Hugh May, Comptroller of the Works, dated
14 March 1676/7 that Morland's engine, by the labour
of a man at 14d a day, supplied water for the King's
household which before cost £60, while the Court was there,
for bringing up the Thames water in carts, and, when
worked by four men, supplied water to the King's great
building there. Also with acknowledgment of Elmer Ellis,
Engineer, dated 25 February 1673/4 that Sir Samuel
Morland's engines are very different from those invented by
himself and that he will not obstruct the passing of an Act
for them.

   This is the first time that we have a clear description of
what the invention consisted. From the constructional point
of view the pump had the great merit for that period that the
barrel did not necessitate boring. The neck was cast with an
annular groove of dovetail section to receive the fillet of
leather which alone made contact with the plunger; the
latter itself was turned, which was a comparatively simple
job. Nevertheless, this must have been the weak point in its
construction, seeing that there was no provision for taking
up the wear of the packing ring, which was either too tight,
causing friction, or became too worn, thus allowing leakage.
The plunger was worked by a rod in the end of a rocking
lever and the two rollers of brass, forming the second principal part of the invention, were guide rollers to keep the
rod moving vertically. Originally Morland seems to have
worked the levers from a crankshaft, but later he replaced

the cranks by cams and rollers, which were carried by the levers.

What happened to the Bill we do not know, probably it was rejected because it was considered that the patent already granted was sufficient reward.

At Windsor Castle further developments took place, perhaps an increase in size and number of the pumps, enabling more spectacular results to be obtained. Contemporary accounts show how great was the interest which the King took in this installation. Space does not permit us to quote all of these, but the more interesting are:[75]

'Windsor July 16. This day His Majesty had a solemn Trial of an Extraordinary Engine lately Invented by Sir Samuel Morland, Knight and Baronet. The Engine being placed in the Plain about 22 Pole from the Foot of the Castle Hill, and being wrought by the strength of 4 Men, forced up the Water through a Leaden Pipe, of an Inch and three quarters Bore into a Vessel plac'd on the Tarras Walk, and Gaged exactly for that purpose, at the rate of above Sixty Barrels an Hour; as His Majesty was pleased himself to measure most accurately by His Majesty's Watch. There are more Experiments to be made and there will be published a more particular Account to contradict those many false Representations and malicious Reflections lately spread by some ignorant scribbling Pamphleteers.'

'Windsor July 30. This Evening the King, Queen and Prince of Orange being attended by divers Foreign Ambassadors, and other Persons of Eminent Quality, and not a few of the English Nobility, together with a numerous train of near 1,000 persons, returning from the Park, Sir Samuel Morland, with the strength of eight men, forced the water (mingled with a Vessel of Red Wine to make it more visible) in a continuous stream, at the rate of above sixty

[75] From the *London Gazette*, July 18–21, 1681, et seq.

Barrels an hour, from the Engine below at the Parkpale, up to the top of the Castle, and from thence into the Air above sixty Foot high, to the great admiration of Their Majesties and all the Beholders, as well Forreigners as others, who unanimously concluded that this was the boldest and most extraordinary Experiment that has ever been performed by Water in any part of the World.'

The culmination of this affair was most gratifying for Morland for the King conferred upon him the title of 'Master of Mechanicks'; the event is thus recorded in the *London Gazette* 1681:

August 14 1681. 'This day His Majesty having sent for Sir Samuel Morland into his bedchamber, (where were present his royal highness Prince Rupert, the Lord Chancellor, the Lord Chamberlain, and divers other great ministers of state and members of the most honourable Privy Council,) was graciously pleased to declare that he was highly gratified with all the late experiments and extraordinary effects of Sir Samuel's New Water-Engine, and therefore as an earnest of his particular grace and favour gave him with his own royal hand, and commanded him to wear it on his breast as a mark of honour during his life, a fair medal of gold, fastened to a green ribbon, on one side of which was His Majesty's effigies, and set with diamonds of considerable value, and on the other side was a Latin inscription. After which the Lord Chamberlain, by His Majesty's order caused him to be sworn MASTER OF MECHANICKS and the inscription on the medal registered.'

We do not find that any salary was attached to the Office of Master of Mechanics, but the office persisted after Morland's time. As to the medal of gold set with diamonds, we have a strong suspicion that this was paid for by Morland himself. To mark the occasion further he had two silver medals struck which he dedicated to the King, at the same time inscribing them to his own glorification. Presumably they were intended for presentation to intimate friends. Very few could have been struck, for they are extremely rare. The only examples we know of are in the British Museum (Nos. 257 & 258): the descriptions are as follows:

257 *Obverse* Bust of Charles II to right, laureate, hair falling in straight curls, no drapery. Inscription: 'Carolo II regi institutori aug. 1681' (To King Charles II, the august founder).

257 *Reverse* 'In adversis summo vitae periculo, in prosperis felici ingenio frequens adfuit' (In adversity at the utmost peril of his life, in prosperity by his happy ingenuity, he was frequently of service). Around the edge: 'Samuel Morlandus Eq. Aur. et Bar. Magister Mechanicorum' (Samuel Morland, Knight and Baronet, Master of Mechanics). Diam. 1.3 in. silver. The die of the obverse of this medal by John Roettier is in the British Museum.

258. *Obverse* Bust of Charles II as before but to left.

258. *Reverse* Inscription: Carolo II Mag. Bri. Fran. et Hiberniæ Regi. (then similar to 257).

Diam. 1.35 in. silver. The die is by George Bower.

John Evelyn seems to have possessed examples of these medals, probably given to him by Morland, and thus refers to them in his *Numismata* 1697, p. 141: 'Upon what Occasion, or whom it does concern I need not inform the World, which has heard of the great and important services Sir Samuel Morland did his Majesty from time to time during the late Usurper's Power by the faithful Intelligence he so constantly gave him.' Evelyn passes on this further remark by Morland with regard to the medals 'which he told me his Majesty gave him leave to wear as an honourable Badge of his signal Loyalty.'

The pump at Windsor Castle continued to work satisfactorily, resulting in further extensions and improvements

being called for. It would appear that the gravitational
supply from Windsor Forest was inadequate for the service
now in prospect and the next step was to draw water from
the Thames; for this purpose a water-house was built by
the riverside and a water-wheel and pump installed, which
forced the water to a reservoir within the precincts. The
cost of this installation, including possibly what had previously been installed, was as we learn subsequently
£2,990 4s. 5¼d.; the detailed accounts of the various crafts-
men are in existence in a minute submitted by Henry Guy,
Secretary to the Treasury, 7 December 1682, directed to the
Officers of the Works at Windsor,[76] asking how the case
stands. The items do not disclose any matter of special
interest and consequently they have not been reproduced
here. Of interest, however, is the fact that on 18 January
following, Sir Christopher Wren was asked to report on
these accounts. He must have demurred at some of the
items, for the delay in payment dragged on for a couple
of years at least. Morland sent in a petition for payment
in 1685 and from this it appears that his first estimate
had been £800 and his explanation as to how the cost
was so greatly exceeded was that it had been proposed at
first to raise water out of the mill river, but the King
finding 'tanned skins and other nastiness in that river' he
(Morland) was forced to make a water-house and a new
engine . . . Being in a hurry and for want of ready money he
had to make bad bargains, with the result that the estimate
was trebled, but 'nothing was done without the King's
privity and approbation.' Morland had received £1,550 on
account, and we believe he eventually received the balance.
It is interesting to note the subsequent history of the water
supply. The plant was put into the care of John Taylor,
carpenter of Eton, who had helped in its erection, at a salary

[76] *Cal. Treas. Books*, Vol. VII.

of £40 per annum and he was still in charge in 1704. In 1690
Morland reported on the plant and a new water-wheel was
made. In 1740 the plant was reported to be in a ruinous state
and that repairs would cost £1,047, so that an entirely new
engine was installed, and rightly so, for the plant had done
duty for eighty years; meanwhile technical progress in
pumps, due largely to improvements in fire-extinguishing
engines, had been considerable.

Fourth Marriage

The untimely deaths of Morland's first three wives did
not deter him from entering once more into the married
state. Possibly he was moved thereto by the fact that, as he
stated in his *Autobiography*, his married life was the only
really happy part of his life. All we know of the event is
contained in a letter from the Lady Anne Howe to the
Countess of Rutland 28 February 1681–82, in these words:
'Sir Samuel Morland lately married a young creature,
daughter to one Frost, a lawyer at Westminster; they say
she was a much greater beauty than any of his ladyes, but
she died of the small-pox, and he was then in Holland, three
weeks ago.'[77] We have no confirmation of this, but the
account is circumstantial and does not read like mere gossip.
It looks as if he had come down in the world socially. The
reference to Holland is obscure, unless it should have read
'France' whither he had gone on the business of the Versailles Waterworks, which will be the main topic of the next
chapter.

[77] *Hist. MSS. Comm.*, MSS. of the Duke of Rutland, II, 66.

CHAPTER V

CLIMAX OF HIS CAREER
1681–84

Accredited to Louis XIV as Consultant for the water supply
of Versailles; High Pressure Steam Engine; Experiments
at Chateau de Maison; Élévation des Eaux

By 1680 Morland may be said to have been at the height of
his reputation as a water engineer. It was no wonder that
Charles II, knowing that his royal cousin Louis XIV was
engaged on a project for raising water from the River Seine
to the level of the Palace of Versailles (a similar installation
to that of Windsor but on a gigantic scale, for Louis wished
to supply not only the Palace but the gardens and the
fountains there), sent Morland over to France to acquaint
the French King with his invention and demonstrate its
applicability to the problems of Versailles. In December
1681, Morland was granted a passport to go over to France
with two attendants.

The scheme that Louis had in hand was known as the
Machine of Marly, so named after the small place of that
name on the banks of the Seine where it was situated. The
installation was planned and carried out between 1681 and
1683 by Swalm Renkin or Rannequin of Liége, a Flemish
waterworks engineer. The water of the Seine was dammed
up by a weir, so as to give a fall of about 3 ft. by which
fourteen waterwheels 36 ft. diam. were actuated. The
power was transmitted by two sets of reciprocating rods
and bell-cranks to 253 pumps in 3 lifts, totalling 502 ft.

above the river, the distance of the furthest pumps being 648 yds. uphill from the river. Just over 100 h.p. was exerted and about a million gallons per day were raised. It was easily the most extensive plant erected up to that time, but it was anything but economical and it was really out of date before it was completed.[78]

Morland in his *Élévation des Eaux*, mentioned below, published in 1685, gives much detail of what took place in France. He states that he arrived there in 1681, i.e. when the Marly scheme was only in the initial stages. He claimed that his scheme was simpler, more efficient because it would raise the water in one lift, and much cheaper than the Marly one. Evidently lengthy negotiations ensued. Morland meanwhile returned to England, for he had on hand another and still more ambitious project for raising water. This was nothing less than the employment of steam as the motive force. His abortive gunpowder engine has been already referred to. We do not know if it was this train of thought pursued further, coupled with the idea of applying the plunger pump, or whether he had some inkling of what the Marquis of Worcester had done previously at Vauxhall.[79]

Towards the latter part of 1682 we learn that 'Sir Sam Morland has lately shown the King a plain proof of two several and distinct trials of a new invention of raising any quantity of water to any height by the help of fire alone.'[80] We may infer that the engine had been conceived and the work of executing it started before Morland left for Paris at

[78] For a fuller account of this famous megatherium of the pumping world, see Belidor, *Architecture Hydraulique*, 1737, translated by Desaguliers, *Experimental Philosophy*, II, 1743, pp. 442–9; and Le Roi, J. H., 'Ancienne Machine de Marly' ou de Ville et Rennequin' in *Memoires de la Société des Sciences Naturelles de Seine et Oise*, Vol. 6, 1861, pp. 106–74.

[79] *Newc. Soc. Trans.*, Vol. XVI, 1936, p. 14, and *Collected Papers of Rhys Jenkins*, 1936. p. 40.

[80] *Cal. Stat. Pap. Dom.*, Charles II.

the end of 1681, and that it was his desire to show it to the
King that had hastened his return. It is clear that Charles had
seen Morland's fire engine at work and had seen it raise
water. The King was deeply sensible of the importance of
any and every new means of effecting this purpose and thus,
at his order, a warrant dated 16 December 1682, was drawn
up for a grant of a patent to Morland. In this warrant the
King refers to the invention as one which 'we are fully
satisfyed is altogether new and may be of great use for the
clering of all sortes of mines and also applicable to divers
kinds of manufactures within our Dominions.'

Having succeeded in producing a fire engine that actually
raised water, one would have expected Morland to have
taken the necessary steps for the issue of the patent and to
have proceeded to make the engines commercially. By this
time, however, Morland was back again in Paris and therefore had to postpone the matter. The strange thing is that we
hear nothing more of the engine, even after his return to
London in 1685. We do not know what became of his engine
and he has not left us any description of it; we conclude that,
like the gunpowder engine, it was an abortive attempt. That
Morland knew something about the properties of steam and
had made experiments with it is proved by what he sets
down in the latter part of his MS.[81] of *Élévation des Eaux*
which we shall have occasion to consider at length later. At
the end of this MS. there is, in a different hand, an appendix
which does not appear elsewhere, entitled 'Les Principes de
la Nouvelle Force de Feu Inventée par le Chev[r] Morland
l'an 1682 et presentée à sa Majesté Très Chrétienne, 1683'
of which the following is a translation:

'The vapours from water evaporated by the force of fire
demand incontinently a much larger space (about two
thousand times) than the water occupied previously and

[81] *Brit. Mus. Harl.*, MS. 5771.

sooner than be imprisoned will burst a piece of cannon. But being well governed according to the rules of statics and by science, reduced to the measure, to the weight and to the balance, then they quietly carry their loads (like good horses) and thus shall become of great use to the human race particularly for the raising of water.'

This is evidence of acute observation on Morland's part. His determination of the ratio of the volume of steam at atmospheric pressure to that of the water whence it was evaporated is wonderfully close to the modern value of 1670 and no more accurate determination was made until Watt, eighty years later, found the ratio to be 1800.

Naturally we wish to know what Morland's engine was like, but we are in the dark so can only make surmises and must be excused for so doing, prefacing our remarks by the statement that the story is a long and involved one.

In the British Museum there is among the North Papers a notebook labelled '*R. North Pictures, Engines & Inventions MS.*'[82] Roger North (1653–1734), son of Sir Dudley North, was a barrister of the Middle Temple. He held the post of Solicitor-General to the Duke of York and, when the latter ascended the throne as James II, that of Attorney-General to the Queen. When William and Mary came to the throne, he declined to take the oaths and retired from public affairs. His elder brother, Francis North, (1637–1685), Baron Guilford, rose eventually to be Lord Chancellor.

Roger North's tastes in boyhood were towards mechanical pursuits and although he adopted the law as a profession he retained these tastes throughout his life. The notebook in question opens with a list of the pictures he owned and it is clear from the context that the list was written before 1701, as that is the latest date mentioned. In the middle of the notebook there are a few pages devoted to mechanical

[82] *Brit. Mus. Add. MS.* 32504.

subjects. North does not mention any names, but we recognise two of the sketches and description as those of Thomas Savery's fire-engine patented in 1698; from what we know of the development of that engine, we can date these sketches in 1700 or 1701. Immediately preceding the description of the above engine we find sketches of a steam engine, in effect a two-cylinder single-acting, high-pressure condensing[83] engine with automatic valve gear. From the pages of the notebook reproduced herewith (see Plates VIII and IX) it will be observed that we have in front of us a clear presentation of the general arrangement. It is headed 'An Engin to doe any works with by ffire & Water.' The cylinders are each marked 'Socket'. In the left-hand cylinder we have the 'plugg sinking down' while in the right-hand the 'plugg' or plunger is 'blewn up.' Midway between the lower ends of the cylinders we see 'Wheelwork to open & shutt ye Stop Cocks alternat' and then at the bottom of the sketch is shown the boiler, containing 'Water' and 'Steam', placed above a 'ffire'. Above the boiler is the inscription 'As this works ye stop cocks open & shutt alternately & so rais & lett ffall the pluggs.' On the next page we read 'The Rising of ye pluggs are ordered to turne a wheel by a toothed barr, wch when at the top, is struck loos by a catch or snack and then ye barr falls downe & with its weight turnes ye wheelwork, wch shutts out ye steam from that pipe or socket, by a stop cock, & pari passu opens the other and then that riseth in like manner, and so they play alternately without help.'

'The uses are derived from the wheel wch these rising barrs work upon, thus alternately as ye occasion is, ffor if a Motion be given either to and fro or continuall, it may be applyed by wheel work to almost all occasions. But this I saw onely in model.'

[83] See footnote (84).

North goes on to tell us that the steam in the cylinder is condensed instantly, but says nothing as to what becomes of the water of condensation. The more important point, however, is that he makes the upstroke of the plugs the working stroke. Possibly he had not quite understood the model, or it may be that his memory had played him false, for it seems that the obvious course would have been to utilise the downstroke, using the steam to raise the plungers against their own weight and the pressure of the atmosphere, and then relying upon the weight of the plungers assisted by the vacuum to perform the working stroke.[84] It is clear that the valves or cocks were worked by the engine itself, although the precise manner in which this was done is not shown. North is careful to note that what he saw was only a model and he gives no indication as to where and when he had seen it, or as to the identity of the maker, so he has left us a puzzle, to whom are we to ascribe this interesting model? It could not be an earlier plan of Savery, for we know that he strongly disapproved of the cylinder and piston engine, because of its supposed excessive friction. Moreover, we have North writing: 'They argue from hence yt the air, pure, & air made by water evaporated are different.' The use of the plural 'they' suggests that he had been in discussion with someone as well as Savery and that the cylinder engine was by another man.

[84] Dr. Dickinson here follows Rhys Jenkins in his opinion that the plugs did their work in turning the wheel by falling under gravity and vacuum. However, it seems to the Editors that this explanation is at variance both with North's explanation and with what we know of Morland's force pumps, which worked at quite high pressures.

The Editors consider that this was in truth a high pressure engine and that the 'toothed barrs' turned the wheel as they rose and then fell back idly, as indeed North says they did. The term 'condensed' could well have been applied by North to the descent of the plugs without condensation of the steam, as he could not have seen what took place inside the 'sockets'. The steam may have been released to the atmosphere.

It could not be a project of Thomas Newcomen who was in the field as early as Savery, because he was directing his experiments along the line of the vacuum produced by condensing steam. We also have Denis Papin, whom we know to have made laboratory experiments, generating and condensing steam under a piston in a cylinder, but there is no suggestion that Papin ever contemplated the use of a plunger, nor from what we know of his migrations between Paris and London does it seem possible that North could have seen any model of his before 1701. By the process of elimination we are thrown back on the surmise that the model described by North was Morland's and that the former had seen it at some period between 1682 and the time of Morland's death in 1695. We know that Roger North spent a great deal of time with his brother, the first baron, Lord Guilford, (i.e. before 1685) and wrote his life.[85] In the course of that work he records that Lord Guilford and Morland 'became good philosophical friends and acquaintance.' Then follows the account of a number of ingenious contrivances, mentioned earlier on page 54, seen on one occasion in Morland's house. The steam engine is not mentioned, indeed it would be unlikely that Morland should have kept it in his house; however, North may have seen it on some other occasion. Later, when he saw Savery's engine, he would recall Morland's and put down a sketch and description from memory.

All this remains highly conjectural but at the same time intriguing. We should always bear in mind that there were a number of men at work at the time attempting to devise heat engines, some from the philosophical aspect of the subject, others in the laboratory and others on a practical scale. The plunger engine may have been due to some unrecorded

[85] *The Life of the Rt. Hon. Francis North Lord Guilford, Lord Keeper of the Great Seal of England*, ed. A. Jessop, 1826, Vol. I, p. 312, and Vol. II, p. 197.

inventor. With this digression we now return to our story based on known facts.

Morland returned to Paris in August 1682. Whether the interval between his first visit and his return had been due to lengthy negotiations with the French King's advisers, or whether he had been attempting to hunt with the hounds and run with the hare, the opportunity came at least for him to demonstrate the capabilities of his new pump.

He was well recommended; for, in 1682, Sir Richard Preston, appointed in that year Envoy Extraordinary to the Court of France, writing to M. de Croissy, says: 'The Chevalier Morland, an English gentleman of rare merit who has an admirable genius and consummate experience in water-works, has come express to offer his services to the King of France and to receive orders from M. de Croissy's brother.' Preston asked for favour and protection for Morland, who was well received for, by order of the King, he was installed in quarters at St. Germain.

At once he immersed himself in the task of putting his plan into concrete form; for instance, on 17 December we find him in conjunction with the Marquis de Blainville determining the weight per cubic foot of Seine water. We can easily imagine that his task, as regards the construction of the pump, was not an easy one for, although French artisans were possibly as clever as any in Europe at that time, the applications were novel. This constructional work was carried out partly at St. Germain and partly in Paris. The place selected for the experiment, judging by what we shall find later, was the Château de Maison near the former place. The experimental or model plant was on a considerable scale, if we can judge by the accounts of the expenditure incurred. When the plant was ready it was shown to the French King, and according to Morland it was successful 'conformément aux demonstrations oculaire et convaincante

G

que j'ai eu l'honneur de montrer au Roi à Saint-Germain en l'année 1683.' The accounts mentioned have been preserved and are entitled 'Divers Payements à compte de Versailles, année 1683.' They date between March and August but are mainly in May and June. The bills of the respective crafts-men are recorded and while it is unnecessary to give them in detail, a dissection under the different craft headings of the total cost is of interest[86] and is as follows: [Translation]

		l.	s.
Woodwork: Joiner		1,100.	0.
Metalwork: Blacksmith, locksmith &			
clockmaker	7016. 10.		
Plumber, for pipes	4240.		
Founder, for body of		25,112.	16.
pump & pulleys	12450.		
Coppersmith	1406. 6.		
Wages to plumbers and other journeymen		4,529.	11.
	Total livres	30,742.	7.

The great preponderance of parts in metal should be noted. This was in keeping with the construction that Morland adopted; timber with him was largely out-of-date. Reckoned at the current rate of exchange (in 1686 it was 123 livres Tournois = £10) the experiments had cost about £2,500 in English currency.

In spite of what Morland says, we conclude that the experiments at the Château were, shall we term it, incon-clusive if not unsuccessful, and that in consequence his plan was rejected. We can well believe that the French King's

[86] Guiffrey, Jules, *Comptes des Bâtiments du roi sous le règne de Louis XIV*, Vol. II, 1681–87, Paris, 1887.

advisers would play for safety and trust rather to the well-tried methods of the bridge waterworks engineers, rather than risk failure with Morland's new-fangled methods for failure would have meant official disgrace.

One of the practical difficulties that must have confronted Morland at an early date was that of taking up the wear of the packing through which the plunger worked. He gives us no hint that he experienced any such difficulty, nor yet any detail of the construction of the packing, much as we should like to know this. We assume that a strip of leather of suitable length was cut from the thickest part of the hide, soaked in tallow, bent flatwise to a circle and the ends sewn together with a cobbler's wax-end. When wear had taken place and leakage became excessive, we suppose that a shaving was taken off the ends and that they were sewn together again. We judge that the packing was a recurring defect that Morland had been unable to overcome, because we do not find that his construction remained in use. He does not seem to have thought of modifying his stuffing box by the addition of a gland with wedges or screws to compress the packing. It appears that his pump went out of use and was forgotten. A different method of packing was meanwhile introduced; this consisted of two hat-leathers reversed to one another along the plunger with a flat ring between them and held in place by similar rings and bolts to the top of the cylinder. This efficient kind of packing is figured by Desaguliers[87] in 1743 but by whom it was invented we do not know.

As a tribute that he considered to be due to the Grand Monarque, and perhaps as a record, Morland prepared the work *Élévation des Éaux* already mentioned. There is a fragmentary MS. in the British Museum (Stowe 748 f. 215 b), said to be in Morland's own handwriting, which ma

---

[87] *Exp. Phil.* Vol. II, 1743, Plate XV. p. 166.

G*

be a first draft. Another MS. is there (Harl. 5771, 20 leaves of vellum 6 in. × 3¼ in.) dated 1683, which is probably the original, for it contains an appendix or dissertation on the use of steam power to which we have referred. This appendix is not included in another MS. dated 1684 in the Bibliothèque Nationale, Paris, which is believed to be the copy presented to the French King, judging by the Royal Arms on the binding and the care with which it has been transcribed. Another MS. (Phillipps 20811) is also known to exist. Eventually the work was published in Paris, permission to print being given 21 February 1685.

In the dedication to the French King, Morland records that His Majesty had been satisfied with models and ocular demonstration which had been shown to him at the Château at St. Germain in 1683; this is only a polite way of saying that Morland's scheme had been rejected. He then goes on to say that the volume contains a summary of the best experiments that he has made during the space of thirty years on the subject of raising water, with figures in profile and perspective, and all that is necessary for the understanding of the profound mysteries of hydrostatics.

In the Preface Morland states that, having employed the greater part of his young days in the theory of mathematics, he began eventually to contemplate with pleasure and satisfaction the beautiful inventions of Archimedes and he gave himself to mechanics with great application and with considerable expense, particularly to the raising of water. 'After having examined maturely during more than thirty years (as much in model as in perspective) the bad construction, the vain multiplicity of unnecessary parts, the great friction and other defects of the major part of the machines that are in use throughout Europe, he had finally the good fortune to discover a construction of piston and pump body quite new and very simple, coupled with a new Cyclo-Elliptical movement, by means of which one might very readily reduce the raising of water to the measure, to the weight and to the balance; and force it at one lift, without coming back, to the summit of the highest mountain at the rate of so many Muyds [a muid = 8 cu. ft. or 561 livres] per hour or of so many cubic inches, according to the moving force given (it may be of rivers or of wind, it may be of horses or of men, it may be of ordinary fire or of that of gunpowder) in a simple leaden pipe resting on the surface of the ground and following all its inequalities and all its winding.' In the light of the reference that has been made above to the steam engine, this is quite significant.

Morland then recapitulates what had taken place in England. His master, King Charles II, had had ocular demonstration of part of the invention and was greatly pleased with what he had seen. A committee of Parliament at Westminster had examined critically his invention and publicly applauded his experiments. His invention had been put into practice during more than seven years in many counties of England on a large scale as well as a small. Lastly at Windsor he had forced water, first by six men to the terrace of the Castle and later by twelve men into the air 80 ft. higher than the parapet; that is to a height of 150 ft. to the amount of 40 muids per hour in the presence of the Royal Family and the Court. Two years previously by the application of a water-wheel to the pumps instead of men, he would have furnished a constant supply of water for the use of the Castle, if his journey into France had not obliged him to leave several parts weak and imperfect.

Morland, continuing, states that a short time previously M. le Président de Maison had done him the honour to ask him to design something for his château, the old machine being broken and rendered useless, and Morland had accepted this employment in order to give His Majesty a sample of how much he knew in hydraulic matters. We hear nothing further about this installation at the Château de Maison, except that the result was not favourable.

Coming now to the body of the work, Morland recounts the experiment that he had made, such as finding the weight of Seine water, the contents of copper pipes of various sizes, lengths, etc. These experiments were carried out at Paris as well as at St. Germain, where he had been established by order of the King.

We now come to the most interesting part of the volume —the description and sketch of the pump and of the 'Cyclo-Elliptical' movement. Morland says that NOR (Plate X) represents in section the pump body, P is the foot valve, LM the plunger, which should be sheathed with copper very exactly turned on the lathe. The plunger rises and falls in the middle of water contained in the pump body and rubs against nothing more than a small circle of leather well prepared which is placed in a small recess at the top end of the pump body on the inside (opposite NO) which makes the plunger slide conveniently in rising and falling without leakage of water and without any sensible friction. To the invention of this he states that he had devoted more than twelve years of study and spent much money. EFGH are weights on the plunger rod; BC are guide rollers. The sketch is, to say the least, inconclusive as there is no means shown for keeping the cover NO and consequently the leather collar in position. The cyclo-elliptical movement (Plate XI) consists of an elliptical cam CLMN centred on the driving shaft which through the intervention of a roller, actuates a lever twenty feet long, from which the pump rod is hung at an intermediate point between the cam and the fulcrum. A number of cams in staggered relationship along the shaft may be used to work several pumps. He states that he made use of this movement for the large machine that he had constructed at the Château de Maison in 1684. This machine had four elliptical cams on the shaft. He says he made these with his own hands and while other mechanics could only raise 30 [cu.] in. of water he raised 100. He mentions also that the height of lift at the Château was 100 ft. The volume concludes with a number of useful tables calculated by the greatest mathematicians of his acquaintance—Pell, Ozanam and Mercator. The letter to Pell asking him to make the calculations is quoted by Halliwell. There are tables of the cubic contents and weight of water in cylinders 1 in. to 12 in. diam.; areas of ellipses; lengths of the hypotenuses of right-angled triangles; weight of water in the tube one pouce (in.) diam. from 1 pied (foot) to 100 toises (fathoms); square roots; cube roots—in fact it was a useful compendium and a kind of forerunner of Molesworth' *Pocket Book of Engineering Formulae*. On the other hand, the whole work leaves the impression in the mind of a certain element of charlatanism and of an unwillingness to give away too much information.

Although Morland had gone to France under favourable auspices, he found himself, after he had been there some while, stranded for lack of money because, as he states in his *Autobiography*, the pensions and other emoluments that he had enjoyed in England were temporarily stopped, presumably on the ground that he would now receive pay and allowances from the French Exchequer, but no such arrangement had been made. The result was that by 1684 he was in such an impecunious state that he had to part with the jewel which the King had given him when appointing him Master of Mechanicks in 1681. Morland appealed to the British Ambassador to supply him with funds. On March 18th 1684, Lord Preston writes to Mr. Secretary Jenkins enclosing a letter from Morland and says: 'His present condition requireth that something be done as soon as may be. Louvois has used him a little hardly, but he doe not think Louis knows anything of it.'[88] On 29 March, Jenkins replies to Lord Preston and in a postscript says: 'Touching Sir S. Morland, His Majesty's pleasure is that you should speak to Mons. de Louvois on his behalf and use the best arguments that Sir Samuel has furnished you with for his fair treatment & satisfaction. His Majesty doth not think fit to write himself . . .' This does not seem to have had any effect and on April 22nd Lord Preston returns again to the subject in a letter to Jenkins: 'I am forced to importune you again upon the account of poor Sir S. Morland.' On 30 April, Lord Preston, short-circuiting Secretary Jenkins, writes to the Earl of Sunderland to this effect: 'I have by the night's post acquainted Sir Sam Morland with His Majesty' bounty to him, for which I am sure he will not fail to make him most dutiful acknowledgment.'

We do not learn what this bounty was but Morland does not appear to have obtained any relief for on 9 August Lord Preston writes again to the Earl of Sunderland and says: 'Sir Samuel Morland hath desired me to enclose this petition, and I hope your Lordship will do him so reasonable a favour as to present it to the King.' Even this does not seem to have had any immediate effect and Morland must have been in dire straits, for on 29 December 1684 we have this long letter from him to Lord Preston: 'What my behaviour has been since my coming into this country your Lordship very well knows, and what my present condition is the enclosed paper will inform you. When I go from hence, if I return into England, then I shall find myself and children after me, by the great severity of the Lords of the Treasury, defeated of the £400 per annum laud of inheritance out of the Lancaster Duchy rents, of which His Majesty made me so absolute a promise above 12 years since. Besides an arrear of 14 or

[88] *Hist. MSS. Comm.*, Vol. VII, MSS. of Sir F. Graham, Bart.

1500£ due to the poor workmen for the engine at Windsor for which they look upon me as responsible and accordingly threaten me. My lord these are but uncomfortable reflections for the latter end of my life.' He asks Lord Preston 'for his mediation with his most sacred Majesty that when he goes from this place his way may be made more easy into his own country.' 'If the King has no service for me, then I would willingly repair into the North and there take my chance among the Coal Mines &c. If my way may not be cleared into England in regard to the fore-mentioned difficulties, then I humbly beg your Lordship to move the King that he would please to give me his letters recommendatory to the Great Duke of Florence, who perhaps may give me bread what little time I am like to live. Probably I may die by the way, and then my prayers will be that His Majesty would be pleased in remembrance of old services to provide for my son, who is now a student in the Temple, according to his quality, and to continue my pensions till such time as they shall have satisfied my private debts.'

Judging from this letter Morland must have been in the very lowest depths of misery. The fact was, to put it charitably, he had fallen between two stools. However, relief was at hand; the representation that he had made must have come to the ears of the Grand Monarque and the latter in his largesse ordered the payment of a gratuity to Morland of 12,000 livres, plus 100 more 'par gratification, en considération de ses services et pour luy donner moyen de s'en retourner en Angleterre.' This meant about £1000 in English money, which one must admit was quite handsome. Now that Morland was in funds, he was in a position to return to England but probably waited to see his work *Élévation des Eaux* through the press before setting out. It was at this juncture that he experienced a severe blow to his fortunes by the death of his patron Charles II in February

1685. Morland was now a sexagenarian and from this time onward can only be considered as a disappointed man. What followed we shall relate in the next chapter.

CHAPTER VI

THE EVENING OF HIS DAYS
1684–95

Removal to Hammersmith; Death of his Patron, Charles II;
Gun Carriage for James II; Fifth Marriage and Divorce;
Opening Letters; Reports on Buildings at Hampton Court for
William III; Blindness; Death; Character

There is now little more to tell. When Morland arrived home from France, he found himself out of employment and we do not hear anything about him for about a year.

In 1684, finding probably that the upkeep of Vauxhall House was too great a drain on his uncertain income—he still retained, although often in arrear, his pension of £500 per annum—perhaps influenced too by the death of his fourth wife,—he decided to retrench and bought a house at Hammersmith. He sublet his lease from the Duchy of Cornwall of Vauxhall which, as we have said, did not terminate till 1705, to Robert Fowles, goldsmith of London, who became the superior tenant from 1696, by arrangement with the executors of the Morland estate. Later in 1699 he obtained a further lease from 1705 of 22½ years. It is of interest to know that the property adjoined the site of the fashionable Vauxhall Gardens. The house to which Morland moved was situated in the Lower Mall. It was subsequently known as Welborough House and at the beginning of the 19th century was occupied as an Academy for the Sons of Gentlemen with the Rev. George Bathie, D.D. as Principal.

In 1685, Morland experienced a shock by the death on 8 February of his patron King Charles II, who for all his waywardness had given Morland many opportunities to show off his talents and had granted him much money to carry his various inventions into effect.

In 1686, Morland made some suggested improvements in gun carriages to improve the accuracy of fire. We learn of it from the State Papers: 15 December 1686. Letter addressed to Pepys:[89]

'Sir, I went about 3 or 4 days since to see what the Commissioners of the Navy have done upon the Order you sent them, relating to the new gun carriages &c., but met with none but Sir Jo. Narborough who told mee your Order express't a Tryal of shooting to bee made like that at Portsmouth, which was impracticable at Dedford, because shooting with powder onley was no Tryall and shooting with bullets too dangerous and therefore his opinion (which hee did beleive would bee the opinion of the whole Board) was that to each new Carriage should be the addition of a Windless, and also the false Truck at the end of the Carriage, and that all the other things as eybolts, Tackles &c. should bee left as they are in the old Carriages till such time as a full Tryall bee made of the new way both at sea, and in a Fight and then what shall proove to bee useless in the old way may bee wholly left off and lay'd aside.'

It is of interest to know that the trials at Portsmouth had been made on board H.M.S. *Royal Charles*. The improvement evidently had involved two journeys to Portsmouth; we hear no more about it; the death of Charles a fortnight before the date of this letter doubtless extinguished all Morland's hopes.

Fifth Marriage

Even if in his previous marriages he had not been influenced by the expectation of receiving marriage portions

[89] *Cal. Treas. Bks.*, VIII. 1073.

with his wives, in his last marriage this was certainly the case and not only so but he seems to have been thoroughly deceived by a tale that the woman, Mrs. Mary Aylif, was an heiress, albeit the daughter of a coachman. He married her on 1 February 1686/7, at Knightsbridge Chapel. Why Morland should have been so credulous as to swallow the gilded bait, we cannot imagine. Not only was the woman deceitful, but she was of bad character and Morland obtained a divorce from her five months later. He tells us about this sordid affair in his *Autobiography*, but unbosoms himself in much more detail to his old friend, Pepys, in a letter dated 19 February 1686/7:[90]

'About 3 weeks or a Month since being in very great perplexities and almost distracted for want of Moneys, my privat Creditors tormenting mee from morning till night and some of them threatening mee with a prison and having no positive Answer from His Majesty about the 1300 *l.* which the late Lord Treasurer cutt off from my pension so severely, which left a debt upon mee which I was utterly unable to pay, there came a certain person to mee whom I had relieved in a starving condition and for whom I had don a thousand kindnesses, who pretended in gratitude, to help me to a wife who was a very vertuous, pious and sweet disposition'd lady, and an heiress who had 500 *l.* per Ann. in Land of inheritance, and 4,000 *l.* in ready Money with the Interest since 9 years, besides a Morgage upon 300 *l.* per An. more, with plate, Jewels &c. The divel himself could not contrive more probable circumstances than were layd before mee. And when I had often a mind to enquire into the truth, I had no power, beleiving for certain Reasons that there were some charms or witchcraft used upon mee. And withall believing it utterly impossible that a person so obliged should ever be guilty of so black a deed as to betray

[90] Howarth, R. G., *Letters and the Second Diary of Samuel Pepys*, 1932, p. 175.

mee in so barbarous a manner, besides that, I really beleiv'd
it a blessing from Heaven for my charity to that person.
I was, about a fortnight since, led as a fool to the stocks and
married a Coachman's daughter, not worth a shilling, and
one who about 9 months since was brought to bed of a
Bastard. And thus I am become both absolutely ruined in
my fortune and Reputation and must become a derision to
all the world.

'My case is at present in the spirituall Court and I presume
that one word from His Majesty to His proctor, and Advo-
cat and Judg would procure me speedy justice, if either our
old acquaintance or your Christian pitty move you I beg
you to putt in a kind word for mee and to deliver the
inclosed into the King's own hands with all convenient
speed. For a criminal bound and going to execution is not
in greater agonies than has been my poor active soul since
this befell mee, and I earnestly beg you to leave in 3 lines
for mee with your own Porter what Answer the King gives
you, and my man shall call for it. A floud of tears blind my
eys, and I can write no more, but that I am

> Your most humble but poor distressed Servant
> S. Morland.'

On the 23 April he wrote to Pepys: 'It has pleased
Almighty God to visit mee with a fitt of sickness.' On 17
May in another letter he recapitulates various attempts to
get rid of the woman by buying her off, failing in which he
is now attempting to prove adultery. On the 19 July he was
able to announce: 'Upon Monday last . . . the Sentence of
Divorce was solemnly pronounced in open Court against
that strumpet for living in Adultery with Sir Gilbert
Gerrard for six Months last past.' She put in an appeal and
Morland entered a caveat, but apparently the appeal was
dismissed and Morland was finally rid of her.

The mention in this letter of 23 April of having been

visited with a 'fitt of sickness' does not tarry very well with the boast that he made to Roger North:[91]

'When he was told that the Lord Keeper North was dead [his death took place in 1685] he asked of what disease? It was answered, of a fever. "It is strange" said he, "that a wise man as he was, should die of a fever." "How," said the other, "should a wise man prevent it?" "By doing as I do," said he; "that is to go to bed with a clyster pipe always in my reach; and that is a box to hold the liquor, the lid of which is a plug that screws down and evacuates it: and from the box proceeds a flexible pipe with the teat at the end; by which, at any time when I find myself not well, I give myself a clyster whereas others are forced to send for help; and in that delay, a fever may hold which might have been suppressed at first." '

Opening Letters

We were familiar during the Second World War with the practice of censoring letters passing through the post and submitted to it with good grace as a necessary war measure. We have to remember that such opening of letters has been practised over a long period, both in war and in peace time, and on several occasions has caused much friction in this country and abroad. We need only cite the evidence of the Comte de Comminges, French Ambassador to the Court of St. James, 1662–65, who, writing to his royal master Louis XIV 8 January 1665, says: 'L'on à ici le secret d'ouvrir les lettres plus subtilement qu'en lieu du monde.'[92] Jusserand says with great truth 'Ambassadors were careful, when using the post, to cipher the more important parts of their letters, a very useful precaution, for packets were constantly

[91] *Life of Lord Keeper North.*, Vol. II, p. 197.
[92] Jusserand, J. A. A. J., *A French Ambassador to the Court of Charles the Second*, 1892, p. 50.

tampered with and there were recrimminations and protests on both sides of the Channel.' . . . Comminges, on his side, relegates to the Marquis de Ruvigny, who is going back to France, the care of informing His Majesty 'of many particulars of which it is dangerous to write. They have here tricks to open letters more skilfully than anywhere in the world. Some even go to the length of fancying that it is the thing to do (cela à le bel air) and that it is not possible to be a great statesman without tampering with packets.' Evidently Thurloe was of this opinion for we find him guilty of the most flagrant use of this practice. Very many of the documents of the Thurloe Papers bear evidence of being copies of letters opened and deciphered in this way and the suggestion is that the practice was carried to a greater pitch in England than on the Continent. One of the duties that was imposed on Morland was the charge of this department of the Post Office. He and a certain Isaac Dorislaus the younger were constituted Members of the Board of Examiners of the Post Office under Cromwell. Evidently they became extremely expert, not only in the opening and resealing of letters without detection, but in copying the contents quickly. This was done by some process which, judging by papers that have come down to us, and by the description, suggests that the offset process of pressing damp tissue paper against the ink (afterwards invented by James Watt for business copying purposes) was that employed.

An abuse quickly leads to a search for a remedy; politicians and others, who wished to ensure secrecy, wrote the whole or the most important part of their letters, as we have seen, in cipher. This led to ingenuity, not only in inventing methods of cipher writing, but also of deciphering it; a simple form of this has been mentioned as the invention of Morland in 1666.

After the Restoration, Morland placed his knowledge and dexterity at the service of the King, and the practice continued unchecked and unabated. We have a circumstantial account from the pen of Morland himself of what was the practice in Charles's time and of the share that Morland had in it when the latter, shortly after the abdication of James II in 1688, submitted to William III, possibly with the ulterior motive of getting into his favour, proposals in detail for carrying on the practice. This occurs in the letter addressed to Lord Shrewsbury, 18 June 1689, in which Morland states that he waited on Major Wildman at the General Post Office on Sunday evening;[93] and has since sent him a paper of proposals by his (the Major's) own agent. He asks for ten or twelve lines in the King's own hand, sealed with his seal, and for five or six sheets of the same paper, and a stick of the same wax. Incidentally he refers to arrears of his pension. A statement of what Morland proposed to do was enclosed—a copy of it is as follows:

1. Offers, at his own cost, to provide engines and utensils, and to discover to the King the true secret of opening letters, counterfeiting hands and seals, and quickly copying long dispatches of foreign Ministers and others, as heretofore discovered by him to Charles II.

2. Offers, at the King's charge, to provide all sorts of engines and utensils which shall be judged necessary by Major Wildman, for putting in practice all the said mysteries at the General Post Office; and to instruct others.

His severe usage in France, and losses since his return, have ruined his domestic affairs. He asks to receive privately the arrears of his pensions, unpaid only by reason of this

[93] *Hist. MSS. Comm.*, 1903, MSS. of the Duke of Buccleuch and Queensberry, Vol. II, p. 48.

late Revolution, as appears by Sir Robert Howard's certificate; also, he asks for a dormant warrant for their payment in future. He must search the city and suburbs for able workmen, but will so contrive that they shall not know what these engines are designed for. He desires the return of this paper. Attached also is Morland's statement or account of what took place in Charles's time in such detail that comment is hardly necessary. The statement is as follows:

(June 1689) 'About two years before the Fire of London, Sir Henry Bennet [afterwards first Earl of Arlington] . . . told me that the Spaniards had a way of sealing up their letters so as it was utterly impossible to open them without being discovered. And having heard that I pretended to those arts, for experiment sake he went into a private room, and wrote ten or twelve lines, and sealed it up after the Spanish manner and gave it to me to try my skill.

'About two days after I waited on him, and having first given him, in a loose paper, a copy of what he had so written and sealed up, I put into his hand his own letter, and four more. All which when he had opened with all the care imaginable, and could by no means find which was his own hand and seal, he immediately left me (being not a little surprised!) and acquainted the King with what had happened and showed him all the papers.

'The King being very desirous to see the operations, a time was appointed, and late at night in the Secretary's office, when all the clerks and messengers were gone, I showed His Majesty and the Lord Arlington the operations of several models in little, with which he was so well pleased, that he sent for the Postmaster-General, and ordered him to prepare two rooms at the General Post Office to put these things in real practice, which in three months after was done; and the King himself, with the Lord Arlington and one more went privately in a coach about eleven of the clock at night to the General Post Office, and there stayed near three hours to see with admiration and very great satisfaction—

1. The manner of opening (and that with great ease and expedition) all manner of seals, as well in wafers as in wax, and then closing and sealing them up again, so as never to be discovered by the most curious eye.

2. The several ways of counterfeiting all sorts of seals, and giving as sharp impressions as with the original seals; which is by most men thought impossible to do, especially in wafers.

3. The counterfeiting all manner of writing, so as to make it impossible for any person to know or distinguish his own handwriting.

4. The sudden and exact copying out of any writing, though it be a whole sheet of paper close written on both sides, for which there is little more than one minute's time required, and so proportionably, be there never so many sheets.

Morland goes on to say that the method was followed at the General Post Office until at the Fire of London the apparatus was destroyed and was not set up again. He then proceeds to point out how advantageous to the King such a system is. 'There were always great clamours made by public Ministers and others for opening their letters by one, Mr. Dorislaus, who had a salary for that purpose, but alas, understood no better ways than to cut letters open with a penknife, and then drop wax under.' There is this note at the end of the paper in Lord Shrewsbury's handwriting: 'The King made a very honourable answer, that Sir Sam. should be considered, but he thought that the secret ought to die with him, as too dangerous to be encouraged.'

How Morland managed to reseal a letter with wax without detection unless he took impressions of the seals in

some plastic material before tampering with them and how
he was able to do it so quickly we do not know. In his
Autobiography he refers to the subject and submitted
examples of what he could do in that line among the papers
which attached to that document. We do not learn of any
further use being found for his methods or for his services.

It is a matter of general knowledge that William and
Mary became greatly attached to Hampton Court Palace and
preferred it to Windsor as a royal residence, probably
because it is more in keeping with that which they had
known in Holland. The Palace was completely reconditioned; the wing and the Dutch garden, so much admired
today, were added by them. Some dispute having arisen as to
the new building, possibly about the wing mentioned, led
to the appointment of Morland in 1690 with two others to
examine buildings alleged to be defective.[94] Possibly the
opening of letters had brought him to the King's notice;
however, we do not know any details of this examination or
the outcome of it.

It is doubtful whether he could have undertaken this task
as, towards the end of the year, blindness unfortunately
began to creep over him. This he mentions in a letter to
Lord Weymouth (1640–1714), one of the four who were
sent to invite William of Orange to England. The letter
was written . . .[95] 'when blind by the help of a ruler' to get
him placed among the exceptions as regards pensions, which
were evidently undergoing revision. The ruler was probably
a kind of frame placed so as to guide the pen in a straight
line; at any rate it was an early example of such an appliance.
The doctor gave him hope of restoring his sight as soon as
the warmer weather came, but this, as we will guess, never
came about.

[94] *Cal. Stat. Pap. Add.*, 1660–70, Book IX.
[95] *Hist. MSS. Comm.*, V, 319, MSS. of Sir A. Malet.

In the last decade of his life he turned for consolation to religion, as is evident by the publication of the apocalyptic miscellany, his *Urim of Conscience*, and by his burying his music books, a real sacrifice in an age when the practice of that art was part of a gentleman's accomplishments. A couple of centuries earlier Morland would have entered a monastery. It may be that this is how he got into touch with Thomas Tenison (1636–1715) later Bishop of Lincoln. Morland never seems to have missed an opportunity of making the acquaintance of anyone who might be of use to him. He wrote to Tenison in 1688 with a proposition to edit a textbook of Euclid's *Elements*, already referred to. On 3 May 1689 he confided to Tenison the '*Abbreviat*' of his life upon which we have drawn so frequently in these pages. No doubt Morland was sincere, and this led to a visit from Tenison, now Archbishop of Canterbury, accompanied by John Evelyn on 28 October 1695, who thus describes the visit in his diary: 'The Abp and myselfe went to Hammersmith to visite Sir Sam. Morland, who was entirely blind; a very mortifying sight. He shew'd us his invention of writing, which was very ingenious; also his Wooden Kalender, which instructed him all by feeling; and other pretty and useful inventions of mills, pumps, &c., and the pump he had erected that serves water to his garden and to passengers, with an inscription, and brings from a filthy part of the Thames neare it a most perfect and pure water. He had newly buried £200 worth of Music books 6 feet under ground, being, as he said, love songs and vanity. He plays himself Psalms and religious hymns on the theorbo.'[96]

Morland was now nearing the end. One of his last acts, alluded to by Evelyn, was to present to the inhabitants of Hammersmith a pump and drinking fountain which remained a boon for many long years. This gift he recorded

---

[96] A large lute with a double neck and extra strings in the bass.

in a tablet fixed to the wall of his house with the following inscription:[97]

'Sir Samuel Morland's well, the use of which he freely gives to all persons; hoping that none who shall come after him will adventure to incur God's displeasure by denying A CUP OF COLD WATER (provided at another's cost and not their own) to either neighbour, stranger, passenger, or poor thirsty beggar, 8th July, 1695.'

Five months later he died on the day after Christmas Day, 1695, and was buried on 2 January following in Hammersmith Churchyard, a chapel of Ease of Fulham, (1629–1854), in a vault for which he had paid the Churchwardens during his lifetime. There is no memorial to him in the church.

Morland had as surviving issue only one son, Samuel, by his first wife, born 1662 or 1663. He was educated at Westminster School and Magdalene College, Cambridge. In 1679 he was a student in the Middle Temple and presumably took up the legal profession. He succeeded as second baronet and, as he died without issue in 1716, the baronetcy became extinct. We judge that the father and son were not on good terms for, by his will dated 25th and proved the 30 December 1695, he left everything to Mrs. Zenobia Hough, of the parish of St. James, Westminster; the haste in obtaining probate is suspicious.

Not long before his death, Morland entrusted his papers to his nephew Dr. Joseph Morland[98], son of his brother Martin, and these are collected in the work *Hydrostaticks*. In the preface the Editor says: 'The following Tables I Received from Sir Samuel Morland, amongst the rest of his Mathematical Papers, all of which Kind he was pleased to bestow on me not long before his Death. As for these which

[97] Lysons, Sir D., *Environs of London*, 1793. p. 414.

[98] Joseph Morland, born 1671; graduated M.D. Leyden 1699; elected F.R.S. 1703; died 1716.

I now Publish, he told me particularly, that they contained
the Mystery of that Art and nimble Dispatch, which he was
Master of, in the Making and Managing of (more especially)
such Mechanical Engines as relate to the Water; in the Improvement of which sort he was so much happier than the
rest of Mankind. He thought that it might be an acceptable
and useful piece of Service to the World, to range these
Materials in good Order; and where there should be
occasion, to add so much light as might make them easily
Intelligible to a Common Reader.

'How I should do this, he gave me large Directions from
his own Mouth, and I have punctually observed them, in the
Compleating of this Piece; so that here are plain and easy
Rules and Directions delivered in a perspicuous manner,
that guide the Practitioner into the Concisest way of Calculation in these Matters . . . What other of his Papers may
hereafter be made Publick, must be left to further Enquiry
and Consideration.   Joseph Morland.'

The Editor did his work conscientiously, but the book
contains little more than a réchauffé of the arithmetical
tables, etc., which we have already noticed in preceding
pages, and do not really 'guide the Practitioner.' The fate of
these papers is unknown; doubtless they were eventually
destroyed.

The Editor says (page 55) 'I must confess that the Author
had very small Encouragement to help our Engineers in
things of this Nature, many of them having dealt very dis-
ingenuously with him; when he had, by near Forty Years
Study and Practice, and the Expenditure of many a thousand
Pounds produced new and better ways of raising Water,
than for ought I know, were ever known to former Ages,
viz. by the means of:

1. A *Forcer* moving up and down in a *Chamber* of
   Water, through a small *Collar* or *Neck* of *Leather*
   fastned in a *Groove*.

H*

2. The *Circular Motion* of a Crank, reduced to a *Perpendicular*.

3. The *Unequal Motion* of a *Crank* exchanged for an *Elliptical Equal Motion*.'

Although Morland was always pleading poverty, very large sums of money actually passed through his hands in the way of pensions, rewards and refund of expenses, the amounts of which it would be tedious to recite but they are noted in the Treasury Books at the Record Office. We are not always certain that he did receive the amounts, which were granted to him and, during the reigns of Charles II and James II, pensions were either deferred or not paid; but in the reign of William and Mary he seems to have been well treated, perhaps as a result of the appeal he made in 1689, for we find a dormant warrant, dated 18 December 1694 for a 'payment of a pension of 600*l*. per annum to Sir Samuel Morland as granted by payment of 1678 Sept. 26, viz. one of 400*l*. per annum and one of 200*l*. per annum out of tenths to be hereby paid by tallies on the collectors of Receivers of Tax. Hereon 150*l*. to be paid forthwith for 1694 June 24 quarter'.[99] This would at least have relieved the necessities of the last years of his life and permitted a decent burial.

Character

Judging from what has been unfolded in our history, we can conclude that Morland was vain and had a high opinion of his own abilities. His employment on missions abroad seems to have cultivated in him habits of show and extravagance that were subsequently ministered to by his wives. He was accused of being a traitor but was no more so than thousands of others at the Restoration.

[99] *Cal. Treas. Books*, X, Part II, 1693–96, p. 864.

Like many men of his time, he served both Commonwealth and King to the best of his ability. It is unfair to
such a man to brand him as a turncoat or a traitor. He was a
public servant, who loyally served the State, whatever party
or faction for the time being controlled the machinery of the
State. His action over the affair of Sir Richard Willis suggests
that he was unwilling to do, or be a party to doing, anything
that would dig still deeper the gulf between the two parties
in the State. There were many moderate men like him; their
motives may have been mixed: self-interest blended with
regard for the true welfare of the community. But many
were sincere; if we call them time-servers, then we must
admit that it was largely thanks to such time-servers that
men were able after 1660 to take up the severed threads of a
common life and weave them once more into a whole cloth.

Morland had no idea of the value of money. He was an
egregious time-server, place-hunter and careerist, like
so many others at that time. Although he was always on the
look-out for a sinecure or a pension, and not unsuccessful
in an uprincipled age, he was always pleading poverty;
yet much money passed through his hands and he lived in
comparative affluence. His talent for invention was considerable and ranged over a wide field, yet we cannot class
him as a great inventor. Nor can we adduce any invention in
particular by which he may be remembered, except perhaps
the packing for the plunger pump; yet this fell just short of
perfection. We can say, however, that he attained considerable eminence as an engineer.

He was certainly uxorious, but was unfortunate in his
married life. In an age of riotous dissipation, headed by the
King himself, we do not find Morland guilty of the dissolute
conduct that he saw around him. We accept the statement in
his *Autobiography* that he 'never frequented either tavern, or
kept in pension women of pleasure'—perhaps not an exacting

standard of morality. Morland was almost childishly credulous—Pepys called him a fool—as is proved by the extent of the honours and rewards that he expected from Charles II at the Restoration, by the way in which he parted with the first pension granted to him, and, later in his life, by his acceptance of the cock-and-bull story of Mary Aylif's fortune, showing that he did not outlive this credulity.

He was a man of weak character, easily swayed by the opinion of others. He held no decided opinions of his own, but swam with the stream. However, he was consistent all his life in placing his own interest first and in extracting the maximum of comfort and safety for himself in a state of society that was undergoing great changes. In the end he went down to 'dusty death' unwept and unmourned. His life left little imprint on his day and generation. He was one of the 'also rans' of the seventeenth century.

APPENDIX I

PORTRAITURE

Several portraits of Morland have survived. Of the six portraits that are known and listed below, only the second and sixth are of real value. He was clean shaven as was then the fashion, and wore the flowing wig which was characteristic of the period. His lips were rather full, we should almost say sensual; perhaps this found expression in his uxoriousness. His nose was prominent, his chin showed determination and the colour of his eyes was dark blue.

1. Etching, by Wenceslas Hollar from a painting or drawing by Gonzales Coques, 1650, now lost. Bust to right, oval $2\frac{3}{4}'' \times 2\frac{1}{2}''$. There is a copy in the British Museum.

2. An oil painting by Sir Peter Lely in the Carolina Art Association Collection, $50'' \times 40''$. Half-length front face, periwig and cloak. This was undoubtedly painted for his *History of the Evangelical Churches of the Valleys of Piedmont*, 1658, as the engraving appears as the frontispiece. Reproduced as the Frontispiece to the present volume.

3. Line engraving by Pierre Lombart after the painting by Lely, $9\frac{1}{2}'' \times 6\frac{3}{4}''$. In 1821 this engraving, reduced to one-half, $6\frac{3}{4}'' \times 4\frac{5}{8}''$, was reproduced by T. & A. Rodd. In his *Anecdotes of Steam Engines* 1827, Vol. I. p. 71 Stuart also reproduced it as a stipple engraving, accompanied by a facsimile of an autographed letter dated 13 May 1658.

4. Line Engraving by B. Reading, similar to the preceding, after the same portrait, $6\frac{3}{4}'' \times 4\frac{1}{2}''$.

5. Line Engraving, no painter or engraver stated. Front face, wig and cloak, half-length. This is the frontispiece to his *Description of two Arithmetick Instruments*, 1673. It is entitled 'Samuel Morlandus Eques Auratus Baronettus necnon Camerae Privatae Generosus.' Underneath is his coat of arms and the motto 'De

gliami gvardia mi dio'; although the first two words are doubtful the motto obviously means 'God Guard me from Danger.' The portrait is characterless and hardly worth attention.

6. Miniature, by Samuel Cooper, $2\frac{1}{2}'' \times 2''$. Formerly in the possession of Bennet Woodcroft, F.R.S., and bequeathed by his widow to the Victoria & Albert Museum, London. Reproduced on Plate XII.

As a matter of interest it may be mentioned that there exists a mezzotint engraving by Richard Tompson, $12\frac{1}{2}'' \times 10''$ of a portrait by Sir Peter Lely of Morland's third wife, Lady Ann Morland (1661–1680).

APPENDIX II

MORLAND'S LITERARY WORKS

The History of the Evangelical Churches of the Valleys of Piemont together with a most naked and punctual relation of the late Bloudy Massacre in 1655 and the narrative of all the following transactions to 1658. Engraved portrait, Fol. London 1658.

A new method of Cryptography.
Fol. London 1666.

Tuba Stentoro-Phonica an Instrument of Excellent use as well at Sea as at Land; invented, and variously experimented, in the year 1670 and humbly presented to the King's Most Excellent Majesty, Charles II, in the year 1671.
Fol. London 1671. A second Edition appeared in 1672.

The Count of Pagan's Method of Delineating all manner of Fortifications Regular and Irregular from the exterior Poligone. Reduced to English measure and converted into Hercotechtonick-Lines by S(amuel) M(orland).
Fol. London 1672.
This is printed in Thomas Venn's *Military & Maritime Discipline*, Book II, p. 61. On p. 65 there is a copperplate engraving entitled *Lineae Hercotectonicae Novae*, Dedicated to Charles II by S. M. dated 1666.

The Description and Use of two Arithmetick Instruments. Together with a Short Treatise explaining and Demonstrating the Ordinary Operations of Arithmetick. As likewise A Perpetual Almanack, and several useful tables.
Presented to His Most Excellent Majesty, Charles II, King of Great Britain, France and Ireland by S. Morland.

Engraved portrait, folding table, 13 copper plates, 10 tables on copper and diagrams.

Sm. 8vo, London 1673.

The title page to the first section reads thus:

'A New, and most useful Instrument for Addition and Substraction of *Pounds, Shillings, Pence, and Farthings*; Without charging the Memory, disturbing the Mind, or exposing the Operator to any uncertainty: Which no Method heretofore published can possibly pretend to. Invented and presented to His Most Excellent Majesty Charles II. . . . 1666 and by the importunity of his very good friends, made publick 1672.'

Internal evidence shows that it was composed in 1671.

The title page to the second section reads 'Machina Nova Cyclologica pro Multiplicatione, *or* a New Multiplying Instrument'. Invented, and humbly presented to the King's most Excellent Majesty, Charles II. By S. Morland, 1666.

The Almanack contains an extra copper plate entitled 'A Perpetuall Almanack invented by S. Morland 1650.'

The Perpetual Almanack and Tables afterwards became what we might term a standard work. It was published by John Playford (1613–93) under the title *Vade Mecum or the Necessary Companion* containing Sir S. Morland's Perpetual Almanack in Copper Plate with many useful Tables proper thereto. London 1679. It ran into 22 editions.

The Doctrine of interest both Simple and Compound explained . . . discovering the errors of the ordinary Tables or Rebate for Annuities at simple interest and rebate of money.

Sm. 8vo, London 1679.

Élévation des Eaux par toute sorte de Machines reduite à la Mesure, au Poids, à la Balance par le moyen d'un nouveau Piston & Corps de Pompe d'un nouveau Mouvement Cyclo-Elliptique, . . . avec huit problèmes de mécanique . . . pour le bien public, par le Chevalier Morland.

4to, 31 copper plates, 110 pp., Paris 1685.

N.B. There is a MS. of what is undoubtedly the original of this, dated 1683, in the British Museum (*Harleian MS.* 5771).

'*Abbreviat of his Life*' or Autobiography, MS. letter addressed to Dr. Thomas Tenison, afterwards Archbishop of Canterbury. Lambeth Palace Library MS. 931, 1689. This was bequeathed to the Library by Dr. Edmund Gibson, Bishop of London, who had been Chaplain and Librarian to the Archbishop and is reproduced in full in Appendix III.

The Poor Man's Dyal with an instrument to set it. Made applicable to any place in England, Scotland, Ireland, &c.
Presumably privately printed (London 1689). The only copy known is in Lambeth Palace Library.
75 copies reprinted for R. B. Prosser, 1886.

The Urim of Conscience to which the Author has had recourse for plain Answers, in his own particular case (as every Man living ought to do) to Four Questions of great weight and importance . . . together with Three Select Prayers for Private Families. By Sir Samuel Morland Kn^t & Bart During his blindness and Retirement.
8vo, London 1695.

Hydrostaticks: or Instructions concerning Water-works, Collected out of the Papers of Sir Samuel Morland. Containing the Method which he made use of in this curious art (Edited by his nephew Joseph Morland, M.D., F.R.S.).
12 mo., 73 pp., London 1697.

APPENDIX III

Abbreviat of his life or Autobiography of Sir Samuel Morland, in a letter addressed to Dr. Thomas Tenison[100] afterwards Archbishop of Canterbury. From the original manuscript preserved in the library at Lambeth Palace.

[MSS. Lambeth, 931, Orig.]

SIR,—I am not ignorant of the various reports of the excessive prodigalities and other sins of my youthful daies, that have now for a long time, been spread abroad by the credulous and censorious world; especially since it has pleased Almighty God of late years, to visit mee with manifold crosses and afflictions which have kept almost as exact time and measure as formerly did Job's Messengers. And farr bee it from mee to act the pharise's part, or plead my innocence, in any other terms.

However I have thought it necessary, (being sensible of my mortality, and knowing well that I address myself to a true Nathaniel, in whom there is no guile!) to make you my Confessor, and to give you an abbreviat of the history of some part and passages of my life, being willing to carry the rest into the grave with mee, by reason of the circumstances of the age wee live in, there to bee buried in oblivion.

Having received my education in Winchester Colledg, I was removed to the University of Cambridg, Where having spent nine or ten years, I was sollicited by some freinds to take upon mee the Ministry, for which fearing I was not fitly qualified, I betook myself to the study of the Mathematicks. Soon after, an occasion presenting itself, I accompanied an Ambassador, (among several other Gentlemen) sent by the protector to the Queen of Sweden. At my return, I was recommended to Secretary Thurlo for an assistant, and in a few months time after, sent by Cromwell as an Envoy to the Duke of Savoy in behalf of the Protestants of the Valleys of Piedmont. And from thence

---

[100] Thomas Tenison, born 1636, became Bishop of Lincoln, 1691; Archbishop of Canterbury, 1694, and died in 1715.

to Geneva, as his Resident, to manage the Affayrs of those poor people together with other forraign Ministers, as likewise to transmitt the Moneys collected in England for their Releif, and to prepare Minutes, and procure Records, vouchers, and attestations, for the compiling of an Exact History of the Waldenses.

That negotiation being ended, and having exposed an Account at my return of the whole transaction to a Select Committee of Gentlemen who were appoynted by Cromwell to examin all particulars and make their Report, as appears by their Certificat marked (A)*, Registered in the Council Books, of which I have the original, I was admitted into the most intimat Affayrs of state; where I had frequent opportunities of taking a clear view of all proceedings from 41 to 56, and so forwards for severall years.

Amongst other Intrigues, I was an ey and ear witnes of Dr. Hewet's being inhumanely trepann'd to death (together with several other persons of quality) by Thurlo and his agents. For instance, one Dr. Corkor was sent by Thurlo to Dr. Hewet to advise him and desire him on the behalf of the Royalists, to send to Bruxels for blank Commissions from Charles 2nd. And when those commissions were come, was ordered to desire to bee employed by him to disperse part of them into several Counties, and to keep the rest by him, which don hee was seized on, together with those Commissions, and condemned by a High Court of Justice, and at last cruelly executed.

I was likewise privy to a design which was carried on by Sir Richard Willis (whom Charles 2 trusted with all his Affayrs in England) from a year before Cromwell's death to the Rising of Sir George Booth (afterwards Ld. Delamar) for giving up the person of His Majesty. At which time, the said Sir Richard Willis, by the appointment of Secretary Scott, and one person more (Thurlo being now out of employment) hired a great house called Weston Hanger, in Kent, moated about, and situated for the purpose, and then advised and pressed Charles 2 with all diligence to come for England, and reside in that house for the better encouragement of those who should rise in arms for his Restauration.

* This paper marked (A) and entitled 'Certificate of the committee for Piemont concerning Mr. Morland's negociations for the protestants of the valleys," is preserved in the same volume, and is apparently the only one now remaining.

To this proposition the King readily consented, and the day of his setting out from Bruxels (as I remembered) was appoynted, and notice thereof being given to Scott by Sir R. Willis, there were several thousands of chosen men Arm'd Cap-a-pé, who had instructions to place themselves round about in woods and as privatly as was possible, and upon the Watchword given that the King was enter'd into the said House, to rush in and murder Him and all his followers in a hurry, so as it might never bee known by whose hand hee fell, which was thought by the Contrivers a much better method, than formally to bring him to a Tryal before a High Court of Justice, as they had don his Father.

Now the horror of this and such like designs to support an usurped Government, and fearing to have the King's blood layd another day in Foro Divino to my charge, (there being no person but myself, and the Contrivers, and the cheif of those who were to act it, privy to it); and calling to remembrance Hushai's behaviour towards Absolom, which I found not at all blamed in Holy Writt, (And yet his was a larger step than mine, I having never taken any kind of Oath or made any formal promise that I ever remember to any of those Governments); as likewise seriously reflecting upon those oaths of supremacy and Allegeance which I had taken during the Reign of Charles I. at Winchester Colledg, I took at last a firm resolution to do my native prince, and the Rightfull Heir to the Crown, all the service that should lay in my power. And here I cannot omitt to observe,

1. That this juncture of time was the darkest Moon of all that King's Reign, a time when hee was in a manner abandoned by almost all his neighbouring princes and states, and miserably betrayed by many of his domestic servants, and some of those in whose hands were all his secrets and principal Affayres. A time when hee was in so great distress for Moneys, that being prest by Sir Richard Willis to send him fifty or sixty pound, as oft as hee sent him over new Instructions, which was usually once a Month (though at the same time hee had much greater summs conveyed to him by my hands in dark nights and obscure places such as the Vine Tavern in Holborn, Hackney Coaches, and the like!) His Majesty was frequently forced to pawn his plate or Jewels, and as I rember, once to sell his Coach horses to supply him. All which misfortunes Sir Richard Willis having enumerated and illustrated in a

Letter of his to mee about the same time to encourage the king's enemies here, pin'd the basket, and closed his letter with this paragraph, verbatim, viz., *And now I know not what power that little King has left him, unless it bee to command his followers to run madd as they please.*

2. This was a time when I lived in greater plenty then ever I did since the King's Restauration, having a house well furnish't, a sufficient number of servants and attendants, a very good Coach and horses in my stables, a revenue of above a Thousand pound per annum to mainteyn it, and several hundreds of pounds of ready money by mee; and a beautiful young woman to my wife for a companion. Now the giving myself up to serve the King was not onely to hazard all this, but to live in dayly expectation of being taken out of my bed or house, and drag'd to the torments, and there had my *flesh pull'd off my bones with red hot pincers;* these were Thurloe's own expressions how they had dealt with mee had they in the least suspected mee.

3. Had ambition been and Titles of Honor been what I aym'd at, whenever the King should bee restored; so little appearance was there at that time of any such Change, and such Characters were then given of the King's person, that to rely upon a promised Honor, would have seemd no other then building Castles in the Ayr, and a Hundred pound for the purchase of a Gartar would have been thought a desperate Adventure.

4. Had Gold been the God I then worship't, I had fayr opportunities, as its well known whilst I resided at Geneva, to have gone away with about Twenty Thousand pounds into some remote Corner of the world, where the power then in being could never have reacht mee. Or I might have accepted at my Return of a much greater sum to have timely discovered the whole design of Cromwell's Expedition into the Indies for the Spanish Gold; all those Commissions and Instruments being either in my view or in my custody.

Whoever shall seriously consider the foregoing observations will hardly believe that any self ends, (though possibly they might, by the pravity of man's nature, and the subtilty of the Divel, bee injected into the Fancy) could possibly outwey the considerations of duty and conscience in such an undertaking as this of mine was, in the blackest and worst of times.

Having now resolved upon the end, the next thing was to contrive the means of effecting it. And having made choise of one Major Henshaw, (whose life I had some time before saved, hee being one of the forty men who had sworn neither to eat or drink till they had killed Cromwell) I gott him to send a Letter to Charles 2nd. by one of his confidents, to acquaint him that there was death in the pott, if ever hee entered within the doors of Weston Hanger. This Letter happened to bee put into his hands, as hee had one of his boots already on, and was drawing on the other, to ride post towards the water side, in order to his coming over, as Sir Richard Willis had advised him, for the encouragement of his party. This Letter putt a stop to his journey, but with much difficulty, the King being made almost believe, by the Lord of Ormond and others, that this was onely a strategem of the protector, to throw dirt upon his beloved favourite, and so to spoyl his best Design.

However, the king sent mee an answer marked (B), whereupon I dispatch't Major Henshaw himself, with a second letter, and accompanied it with several long letters, all written with Sir Richard Willis his own hand, discovering from time to time all the King's secrets, and whatever His Majesty had entrusted him with.

To this the King sent mee a second Letter marked (C).

With one of these letters came a privat paper, as from the King (but in truth from the Chancellor himself), ordering mee to send him in another privat paper an account of *His Chancellor Hyde, and what I knew of him*, for hee was then accused of corresponding with Thurlo, and receiving Moneys from Cromwell. I believing it came really from the King, sent such an Account as it seems did not very well please his Lordship. And Hinc illæ Lachrimæ! From that time hee became a mortal enemy.

When I went over to Breda, upon the King's Restauration, The Chancellor charged mee *not to ask any thing of the King, till hee came into England, His Majesty being resolved to give mee more then in modesty I could petition for*. But when I had wayted in England till all things of moment were given away, and at last desired to know what the King designed for mee, his answer was, *zounds! what the Divel would you have?*

Before the King's coming over, by Major Henshaw's and his confidents privat agreement, as I believe with the Chancellor, my wife was made believe that there was a patent brought over and hid under ground to give mee the Gartar, and make her a Dutchess, as being descended from a Noble Family in Normandy, which was a truth, and they had so far possest her with this vain imagination, that shee, desiring mee to walk with her privatly into the garden of my Countrey house, a little beyond Bow, she *conjured mee upon her knees in the face of Heaven to promise and swear to grant her a certain request, which was never to ask any thing of the king but let him do as hee pleased.* And when I pleaded with her, and foretold her what really fell out afterwards, her answer was this—*The misfortune fall upon mee and my children!*

The King being restored, all his promises ended in a patent for a Baronetcy and a Gentleman's place of the Privy Chamber, which was onely a place of great expence, and cost mee at the Coronation 450 pounds in two days. And after I had, *by the Chancellor's order as from the King* delivered up the first Letter into His Majesty's own hand, where hee had promised mee the Garter, &c., I had given mee a pension of 500 pounds per annum out of the post office. But being forced to live at a great expence, and lay out great sums in taking out patents and riding at the Coronation, &c., and so run myself in debt, there was one sent to mee to give mee an Alarm, that the Duke of York would have the post office settled on him, and my pension would bee lost, and I should do prudently to sell it, and there was a Chapman for it, which was Sir Arthur Slingsby, who had it for a sum much beneath its value, and as I heard afterwards, hee bought it for the Lady Green, with the King's Money.

Now finding myself disappoynted of all preferment and of any real estate, I betook myself to the Mathematicks, and Experiments such as I found pleased the King's Fancy. And when I had spent 500*l.* or 1000*l.*, gott sometimes one half, sometimes 2 thirds of what I had expended. Sometimes I had pensions, sometimes none. And care was taken by the Ministers of State (under whom I was forced to truckle, wayting oft at their doors among the footmen) that one thing should bee spent before I gott another. One while I was made a Commissioner of Excise, paying part of it to one who had procured it. But in a few years being run in debt by chargeable experiments I was forced to part with it. At last, with much ado, I gott those pensions that I have of late years enjoyed, but they being very often stopt, I was at a great loss and expence, borrowing money at 50 in the hundred and so anticipating my pension.

About two years before the King's death, hee sent mee into France about that King's water-works, and I borrowed near a Thousand pound upon my pension (to repay the double to those who lent it) to prepare Models and Engines of all kinds for that expedition. But I was no sooner arrived there but the Lord of the Treasury *by his Majestyes permission* stopt all my pensions for three years.

King James did indeed at my return (which was with the loss of above 1300 pistoles,[101] as may appear by the French King's Answer to my last petition marked D) take oft the stop off my pension, and ordered the payment of the Arrears, but permitted the Lord Treasurer Rochester to cutt off above 1300*l*. to pay the Workmen for the Engin that serves Windsor Castle with Water upon the Account of some boons, and some reimbursments I had gott of King Charles in about a year and a half's time before my going over into France. And one of the boons was 150*l*. which payd for the jewel hee gave mee for pleasing him with the engine, and in remembrance of old Services, which jewel I was forced to pawn and part with at Paris to furnish myself with money to bring mee back to England.

As an addition to all these misfortunes, having charitably redeemed a certain woman (whose moralls I then knew not at all) from perishing in a prison, was inhumanely betrayed by her, under a pretence of gratitude, into a vain expectation of marrying an Heiress of 20 thousand pound. And swallowing too greedily the gilded bait, it proved my utter ruin.

I know it is objected against mee, that I have been extravagant in expences with several wines. And I must confess, that was the only content I had in the world, all other things proving cross and full of trouble and bitterness. Besides that, I never frequented either tavern, or kept in pension women of pleasure. And what money ever came to my hands, excepting about 6 or 700*l*. per annum, in my Family or relating thereto, went amongst workmen of all sorts, for Engins and chargeable experiments to please and divert His Majesty; Or else for secret services which were often very considerable sums. Somewhat may bee judg'd by the paper (E). I am sure I have now hardly left ten shillings in the world.

101 An old Spanish gold coin.

After all, I would fain retire and spend my life in a Christian Solitude, and heartily beg you to lend me your helping hand, to have my condition truly represented to His Majesty, whereby you will highly and for ever oblige

Your most affectionate, humble and faithfull servant,

S. MORLAND.

May 3rd. 1689.

P.S.   There is one thing that I omitted in the abbreviat of my own history, which is, that when I did engage to serve the late King Charles 2nd, and did reveal some conspiracy against his life, yet at the same time I plainly sent him word that it was upon condition, *that I might never be call'd to bear witness against any of the conspirators, if upon his restauration, they should happen to bee arraigned at the barr of justice.* And when Sir H. Vane was ordered to bee brought to his tryall, the Attorney-Generall did indeed send for mee, and did very much press mee in privat (and that in the King's name) that I would appear as a witness against him, forasmuch as His Majesty had been informed that I was privy to many transactions, where the said Sir Henry Vane was principally concerned, that would by the law of England bee adjudged high treason. But my answer to him was this, that I hoped His Majesty would remember his promise, *that not a hair of their heads should ever be toucht upon any account. Besides that I would rather be prest to death than come in judgment against either him or any other, whose designs I had formerly discovered.* And thereupon went home to my house, and burnt a certain sheet of paper all written with Sir H. Vane's own hand (which was a draught of a model of a new government with severe reflections on monarchy), as also several other papers, which would have been great evidence against him.

APPENDIX IV

I. BOOKS AND MONOGRAPHS

(Published in London unless otherwise stated)

1. *Robert Fulton, Engineer and Artist.* John Lane, 1913. 348 pp.
2. *John Wilkinson, Ironmaster.* Ulverston: Hume Kitchin, 1914. 60 pp.
3. The early days of canals, railways and locomotives. (Lecture). [New York], 1923. 14 pp.
4. The use of steam power. Address delivered on the occasion of the centenary celebration of the Delaware & Hudson Co. [New York], 1923. 12 pp.
5. *Stationary Engines.* Catalogue of the collection in the Science Museum, with descriptive and historical notes and illustrations. H.M.S.O., 1925. 188 pp., 11 pl.
6. *James Watt and the Steam Engine.* The memorial volume prepared for the Committee of the Watt Centenary Commemoration at Birmingham, 1919. [With Rhys Jenkins]. Oxford: Clarendon Press, 1927. 432 pp., 114 pl., 42 ill.
7. *The Garret Workshop of James Watt.* (*Science Museum Technical Pamphlet* No. 1). H.M.S.O., 1929. 24 pp., 4 pl.
8. *Richard Trevithick: the Engineer and the Man.* (Trevithick Centenary Commemoration Memorial Volume). [With Arthur Titley]. Cambridge University Press, 1934. 308 pp., 18 pl.
9. *James Watt, Craftsman and Engineer.* Cambridge University Press, 1935. 224 pp., 17 pl.
10. *Matthew Boulton.* Cambridge University Press, 1936. 232 pp., 14 pl.

11. *A Short History of the Steam Engine.* Cambridge University Press, 1938. 272 pp., 10 pl. 2nd edition 1963, Frank Cass & Co.

12. *James Watt and the Industrial Revolution.* (For the British Council). [With H. P. Vowles]. Longmans Green, 1943. 64 pp. 2nd edition, 1948.

13. *A History of the Institution of Mechanical Engineers 1847–1947.* By R. H. Parsons. 1947. First chapter on the Background of the Institution contributed by H.W.D.

14. Teaching Notes [for use with film strips]. Three parts of a series on the Industrial Revolution. (General Editor, G. D. H. Cole). Common Ground Ltd., 44 Fulham Road, S.W.3.

    (i) Coal mining: historical. Typescript, 4to, 2 pts. [? 1948–49]. Pp. 20 and 22.

    (ii) Iron and Steel: historical. Typescript, 4to, 2 pts. [? 1948–49]. Pp. 20 and 18.

    (iii) Water supply: historical. Typescript, 4to, 2 pts. [1948–49]. Pp. 20 and 22.

15. *The Cornish Engine.* A chapter in the history of steam power. Description of a series of films produced by the Shell Film Unit, London, with the co-operation of the Cornish Engines Preservation Society. Art and Technics, 1950. (Text written by H.W.D.) 46 pp. New ed. 1951 [1952].

16. A catalogue of the Civil and Mechanical Engineering Designs 1741–1792 of John Smeaton, F.R.S., preserved in the Library of the Royal Society. [With A. A. Gomme]. (Newcomen Society: Extra Publication No. 5). 1950. 202 pp.

17. Twenty-six articles (mainly biographies) contributed to Chambers's Encyclopaedia, New edition, 1950. [Contributions in every volume (except vols. 3, 5, 11, and 12), including biographies of Arkwright, Maudslay, Montgolfier, Murdock, R. F. Mushet, Lewis Paul, Gilchrist Thomas, and Whitworth].

18. Thomas Newcomen, Engineer, 1663–1729. Dartmouth New-comen Association, 1929. (New edition, revised by Percy Russell, 1952).

19. *Water Supply of Greater London*. H. W. Dickinson Memorial Volume. Courier Press 1954; 146 pp. 20 pl. 43 ill. Compiled from original articles by H.W.D. in *The Engineer*, 1948. (See No. 81 below).

II. PAPERS AND ARTICLES

(Dickinson made frequent contributions to the discussions on Papers read before the Newcomen Society, and also to both the 'Queries' and 'Replies' columns of 'Notes and Queries', and he wrote many book reviews for the 'Museums Journal' and other periodicals. With very few exceptions, none of these contributions has been included in the list below).

1. John Wilkinson, Ironmaster. *Engineering*, Vol. 86, 1908, Dec. 4, pp. 741–742.

2. Business Aspects of Early Engineering. *The Engineer*, Vol. 106, 1908, Dec. 25, p. 670.

3. Ealing or easing hearth. *Notes and Queries*, 10th Series, Vol. 11, 1909, Jan. 30, pp. 87–88; 11th Series, Vol. 8, 1913, Aug. 9, p. 114.

4. Matthew Boulton, F.R.S. *Engineering*, Vol. 88, 1909, Aug. 13, pp. 224–226.

5. John Wilkinson [Life and Work]. *Beiträge zur Geschichte der Technik*, Bd 3, 1911, pp. 215–238.

6. Some unpublished letters of James Watt. *Proc. Institution of Mechanical Engineers*, 1915, pp. 487–534.

7 Tread-mill at Carisbrooke Castle. *Engineering*, Vol. 100, 1915, Sept. 10, p. 260.

8. Chanelhouse; Ion: Ormondy: Twisaday. [Surnames in Furness]. *Notes and Queries*, 12th Series, Vol. 1, 1916, April 1, p. 274.

9. Centenary of James Watt: his Life and Work: the Evolution of the Steam Engine. *The Observer*, 1919, Aug. 24, p. 11 (2 cols).

10. An 18th century Engineer's Sketch Book. [W. Reynolds's Sketchbook, c. 1792–1803.] *Trans. Newcomen Society*, II, 1921–22 (1923), pp. 132–140.

11. John Planta's Spinning Wheel. *Notes and Queries*, Series 12, Vol. 10, 1922, March 11, p. 189; Series 13, Vol. 1, 1923, Aug. 25, p. 155.

12. The Rastricks—Civil Engineers. [With A. Lee]. (Paper read, 5 March 1924). *Trans. Newcomen Society*, IV. 1923–24 (1925), pp. 48–63.

13. An Engineer's Sketch-book of the 18th Century [W. Reynolds, 1758–1803, of the Ketley Ironworks, Shropshire]. *The Engineer*, Vol. 135, 1923, Jan. 19, pp. 59–60.

14. Opening of the Deutsches Museum, Munich. *The Museums Journal*, Vol. 25, 1925–26, pp. 8–11, 43–48.

15. Memorial to Charles Wheatstone in St. Michael's Church, Gloucester. *Trans. Newcomen Society*, V. 1924–25, (1926), p. 99.

16. The Science Museum. *Mechanical Engineering*, Vol. 48, 1926, pp. 104–105.

17. Landmarks in the history of Prime Movers. *Mechanical Engineering*, Vol. 48, 1926, pp. 1385–1388; correspondence, Vol. 49, 1927, p. 179.

18. Obituary notice of John Lockhart Brunton. *Trans. Newcomen Society*, VI. 1925–26 (1927), pp. 228–229.

19. Industrial Revolution. *Nature*, Vol. 119, 1927, June 4, p. 818.

20. Samuel Crompton, 1753–1827: a biographical note and an introduction. In Official Record of Annual Conference of the Textile Institute held at Bolton, 7th–10th June, 1927, in association with the Samuel Crompton centenary celebration. Special issue of the Journal of the Textile Institute, July 1927, pp. 7–13. (Abstract in *The Textile Recorder*, Vol. 45, 1927, June, pp. 82–84).

21. The New Buildings of the Science Museum. *The Museums Journal*, Vol. 27, 1927–28, pp. 336–341.

22. Obituary notice of Alfred Rosling Bennett, Pioneer of the Telephone. *Trans. Newcomen Society*, VII, 1926–27 (1928), pp. 151–152.

23. A Puzzle in Pottery [On some curious pots unearthed in Lincolnshire]. (Letter). *The Museums Journal*, Vol. 28, 1928–29, p. 212.

24. The Atmospheric Railway. (Letter). *The Museums Journal*, Vol. 28, 1928–29, p. 403.

25. [On Platform Weighing-Machines]. *Trans. Newcomen Society*, IX, 1928–29 (1930), pp. 73–76.

26. Thomas Newcomen, Father of the Steam Engine. *The Engineer*, Vol. 148, 1929, p. 101.

27. Museums and Education. Address on May 30, 1929, to Purley Rotary Club. Short report in *The Museums Journal*, Vol. 29, 1929–30. p. 31.

28. Diary of John George Bodmer, 1816–1817. *Trans. Newcomen Society*, X, 1929–1930 (1931), pp. 102–114.

29. Thomas Newcomen und seine Dampfmaschine. Ein Rückblick auf die Zeit vor 200–Jahren. *Beiträge zur Geschichte der Technik*, Bd. 19, 1929, pp. 139–143.

30. The Invention of the Steam Hammer. *Mechanical Engineering*, Vol. 51, 1929, pp. 445–447; *Heat Treating and Forging*, Vol. 15, 1929, pp. 846–848.

31. Jolliffe and Banks, Contractors. (Paper read 14 October, 1931). *Trans. Newcomen Society*, XII, 1931–1932 (1933), pp. 1–8.

32. [Straw-plaiting in Hertfordshire]. *Trans. Newcomen Society*, XII, 1931–32 (1933), p. 29.

33. J. O. Halliwell and the Historical Society of Science (London, 1841). *Isis*, Vol. 18, 1932, pp. 127–132.

34. The Shetland Watermill. [With E. Straker]. (Paper read 25 February, 1933). *Trans. Newcomen Society*, XIII, 1932–33, (1934), 89–94.

35. Memorials to Pioneers. (Letter. Part of correspondence on the Memorial Windows to Stephenson, Locke, and Siemens, in Westminster Abbey). *Engineering*, Vol. 135, June 30, 1933, p. 713.

36. Museums and their relation to the history of Engineering and Technology. Presidential Address, Oct. 11, 1933. *Trans. Newcomen Society*, XIV, 1933–34 (1935), pp. 1–12.

37. Obituary notice of Lucien Alphonse Legros. *Trans. Newcomen Society*, XIII, 1932–1933 (1934), pp. 203–204.

38. Obituary notice of Thomas Clarkson. *Trans. Newcomen Society*, XIII, 1932–1933 (1934), pp. 202–203.

39. Robert Fulton's original drawings, by Frederick D. Herbert. With a memorandum on the drawings by H. W. D. *The Engineer*, Vol. 158, 1934, Nov. 23, pp. 511–512.

40. Obituary notice of Oskar von Müller, Director of the Deutsches Museum, Munich. *The Museums Journal*, Vol. 34, 1934–35. pp. 76–79.

41. Evolution of Invention (Part of symposium). *Proc. Institution of Mechanical Engineers*, Vol. 126, 1934, pp. 3–11; *Metal Industry* (London), Vol. 44, 1934, pp. 179–182.

42. Alte Strassen und Pflasterungen in London. *Technik-Geschichte*, Bd 23, 1934, pp. 45–50.

43. Many Inventions. A lecture to the Institute of Patentees, Feb. 20, 1935. *The Inventor*, Vol. 6, 1935, March, pp. 86–87; April, pp. 100–101.

44. Obituary notice of William Sisson. *Trans. Newcomen Society*, XV, 1934–35 (1936), p. 254.

45. Obituary notice of J. G. H. Warren. *Trans. Newcomen Society*, XV, 1934–1935 (1936), pp. 255–256.

46. [Johann Georg] Bodmers technisches Werk. *Neue Zürcher Zeitung*, 1936, Dezember 6. And an Italian translation as 'L'Opera tecnica di Bodmer' in *La Svizzera Industriale e Commerciale*, Anno I, No. 1, 1938, Febbraio. (Offprints from both journals were issued).

47. The Museum in Germany To-day [1936]. (Letter). *The Museums Journal*, Vol. 36, 1936–37, p. 368.

48. William Wilkinson. *The Engineer*, Vol. 163, 1937, May 28, p. 617.

49. Early Years of the Hydraulic Ram. (Paper read Jan. 20, 1937). *Trans. Newcomen Society*, XVII, 1936–37 (1938), pp. 73–83.

50. The Farey Diary 1819, annotated by H. W. Craver, H. W. D., and Rhys Jenkins. *Trans. Newcomen Society*, XVII, 1936–37 (1938), pp. 215–219.

51. The History of Vitriol Making in England. (Paper read Dec. 15, 1937). *Trans. Newcomen Society*, XVIII, 1937–38 (1939), pp. 43–60.

52. Charcoal and Pyroligneous-acid Making in Sussex. [With E. Straker]. (Paper read Dec. 15th, 1937). *Trans. Newcomen Society*, XVIII, 1937–38 (1939), pp. 61–66.

53. Elinghearths. *Trans. Newcomen Society*, XVIII, 1937–38 (1939), pp. 274–276.

54. The Lewin Diary, a link with Rennie. [William Lewin, 1794–1863]. (Paper read, Feb. 8, 1939). *Trans. Newcomen Society*, XIX, 1938–39 (1940), pp. 109–117.

55. Bicentenary of Henry Cort. *Nature*, Vol. 146, 1940, pp. 722–723.

56. Henry Cort's Bicentenary. (Abstract read, Nov. 13, 1940). *Trans. Newcomen Society*, XXI, 1940–41 (1943), pp. 31–47.

57. Origin of Gauges for Wire, Sheets, and Strip. [With Henry Rogers]. (Paper read, Jan. 15, 1941). *Trans. Newcomen Society*, XXI, 1940–41 (1943), pp. 87–98.

58. Obituary notice of Leonor Fresnel Loree. *Trans. Newcomen Society*, Vol. XX, 1939–40 (1941), p. 179.

59. James Nasmyth as a Tool Maker. *The Engineer*, Vol. 171, 1941, May 23, pp. 337–339.

60. Origin and Manufacture of Wood Screws. (Paper read Dec. 10, 1941). *Trans. Newcomen Society*, XXII, 1941–42 (1946), pp. 79–89.

61. Robert Stuart Meikleham. [With A. A. Gomme]. (Paper read March 11, 1942). *Trans. Newcomen Society*, XXII. 1941–42 (1946), pp. 161–167.

62. Joseph Bramah and his Inventions. (Paper read April 22, 1942). *Trans. Newcomen Society*, XXII, 1941–42 (1946), pp. 169–186.

63. Cutting Quill Pens [Cutting instrument attributed to Joseph Bramah]. (Letter). *The Ironmonger*, Vol. 215, 1942, p. 252.

64. Monger or Merchant. [On the origin of the word 'Monger']. *The Ironmonger*, Vol. 215, 1942, p. 301. [unsigned].

65. A Condensed History of Rope-making. (Paper read Jan. 13, 1943). *Trans. Newcomen Society*, XXIII, 1942–43 (1948), pp. 71–91.

66. The Kodak Museum of Photography. *The Museums Journal*, Vol. 43, 1943–44, pp. 130–131.

67. Utilization of Waste Heat from Industrial Operations. (Paper read Oct. 13, 1943). *Trans. Newcomen Society*, XXIV, 1943–45 (1949), pp. 1–11.

68. A Study of Galvanised and Corrugated Sheet-metal. (Paper read Dec. 16, 1943). *Trans. Newcomen Society*, XXIV, 1943–45 (1949), pp. 27–36.

69. Man's Quest for Mechanical Power. Presidential Address, Jan. 15, 1944. *Proc. Croydon Nat. Hist. and Scientific Soc.*, Vol. 11, 1935–1948, pp. 171–178.

70. The Bicentenary of the Platform Weighing-Machine. *The Engineer*, Vol. 178, 1944, Dec. 29, pp. 504–506.

71. Britain's Contribution to the Iron and Steel Industries. *Edgar Allen News*, Vol. 22, 1944, pp. 262–263, 275–276.

72. Besoms, Brooms, Brushes, and Pencils: the Handicraft Period. (Paper read Nov. 15, 1944). *Trans. Newcomen Society*, XXIV, 1943–45 (1949), pp. 99–108.

73. A Museum for Croydon. Presidential Address, Jan. 23, 1945. *Proc. Croydon Nat. Hist. and Scientific Soc.*, Vol. 11, 1935–1948, pp. 203–208.

74. Development of the Stone-breaker. *Edgar Allen News*, Vol. 23, 1945, pp. 390–392.

75. How the Cornish Engine came to London. Paper read to Cornish Engines Preservation Society, May 25, 1946. *Engineering*, Vol. 161, 1946, May 31, p. 510.

76. Factors in Industrial Relations [Prospects for Great Britain]. *Mechanical World*, Vol. 120, 1946, Sept. 20, p. 326.

77. Richard Roberts: his Life and Inventions. (Paper read Nov. 13, 1946). *Trans. Newcomen Society*, XXV, 1945–47 (1950), pp. 123–137.

78. Machine Tools in 1847. *Engineering*, Vol. 163, 1947, June 6, p. 468.

79. Tercentenary of Denis Papin [Report of French celebrations]. *The Engineer*, Vol. 164, 1947, Aug. 1, p. 111.

80. The Tercentenary of Denis Papin. *Nature*, Vol. 160, 1947, Sept. 27, pp. 422–423.

81. Water Supply of Greater London. *The Engineer*, Vol. 186, 1948, July 9 and weekly to December 10, pp. 26–27, 50–53, 76–78, 100–102, 126–127, 150–151, 176–177, 206–208, 232–234, 255–257, 276–279, 300–302, 326–328, 352–354, 378–381, 404–407, 430–433, 456–458, 482–484, 508–511, 534–536, 560–561, 586–587. Issued in book form as H. W. Dickinson Memorial Volume, 1954.

82. Eulogy of Trevithick at unveiling of Memorial at East Pool, Cornwall, Oct. 16, 1948. *Engineering*, Vol. 166, 1948, Oct. 22, p. 403.

83. William Ford Robinson Stanley: Founder Member and benefactor. (Paper read March 24, 1949). *Proc. Croydon Nat. Hist. and Scientific Soc.*, Vol. 12, 1948–1951, pp. 51–59.

84. Obituary notice of Conrad Matschoss. *Trans. Newcomen Society*, XXIV, 1943–45 (1949), p. 173.

85. Indicating Old Steam Engines [Trial of engines at Crofton Pumping Station]. *The Engineer*, Vol. 188, 1949, Oct. 14, p. 433. [Unsigned].

86. Memorial to Richard Trevithick and J. U. Rastrick at Bridgnorth, Shropshire. *Engineering*, Vol. 168, 1949, Dec. 2, p. 584.

87. Netherlands contributions to Great Britain's Engineering and Technology to the year 1700. [With A. A. Gomme] (Read at Summer Meeting in the Netherlands, May 8, 1949). *Archives Internationales d'Histoire des Sciences*, No. 11, 1950, pp. 356–377.

88. Some British contributors to Continental Technology 1600–1850. [With A. A. Gomme]. (Communication to Sixth International Congress of the History of Science, August 1950). *Actes du VI Congrès International d'Histoire des Sciences*, 1950, pp. 307–323; *Archives Internationales d'Histoire des Sciences*, No. 16, 1951, pp. 706–722.

89. A Brief History of Draughtsmen's Instruments. (Paper read Feb. 8, 1950). *Trans. Newcomen Society*, XXVII, 1949–51 (1956). pp. 73–84.

90. James White and his 'New Century of Inventions' (Paper read

Feb. 14, 1951. *Trans. Newcomen Society*, XXVII, 1949–51 (1956), pp. 175–179.

91. The Taylors of Southampton: their Ships' Blocks, Circular Saw and Ships' Pumps. (Paper read for H.W.D. Jan. 12, 1955). *Trans. Newcomen Society*, XXIX, 1953–55 (1958). pp. 169–178.

INDEX

THE PLATES

PLATE I

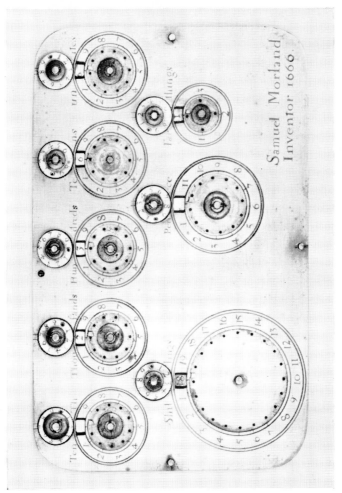

Calculating Machine for Addition and Subtraction, in the Science Museum, London.
See page 29

PLATE II

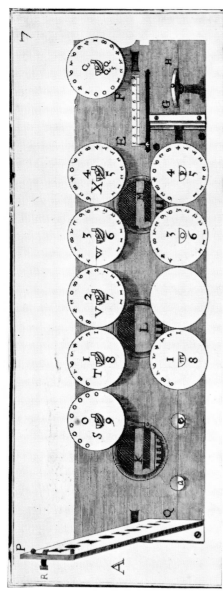

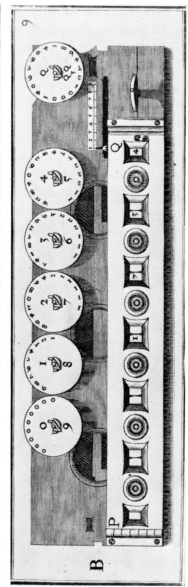

Multiplying Machine. Plates A and B from *The Description and Use of two Arithmetick Instruments*, 1673.
See page 30

PLATE III

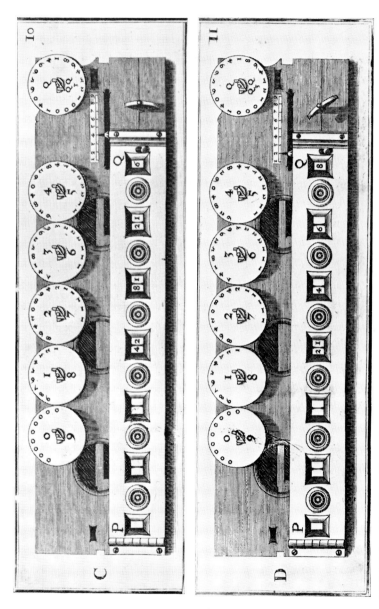

Multiplying Machine. Plates C and D from *The Description and Use of two Arithmetick Instruments*, 1673.
See page 30

PLATE IV

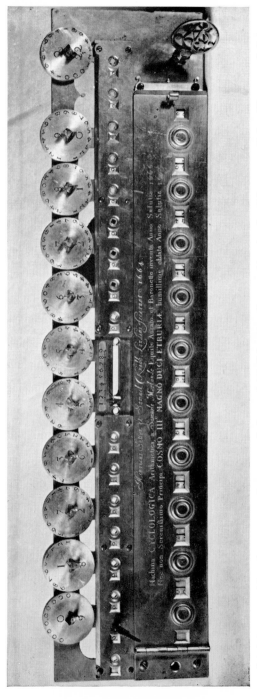

Multiplying Machine by Henry Sutton and Samuel Knibb, London, 1664, in the Museum of the History of Science, Florence.

See page 30

PLATE V

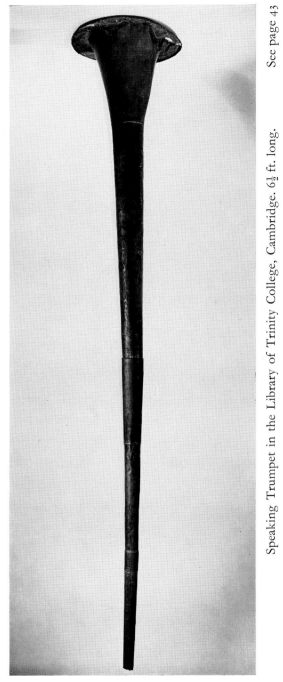

Speaking Trumpet in the Library of Trinity College, Cambridge. $6\frac{1}{2}$ ft. long.

See page 43

PLATE VI

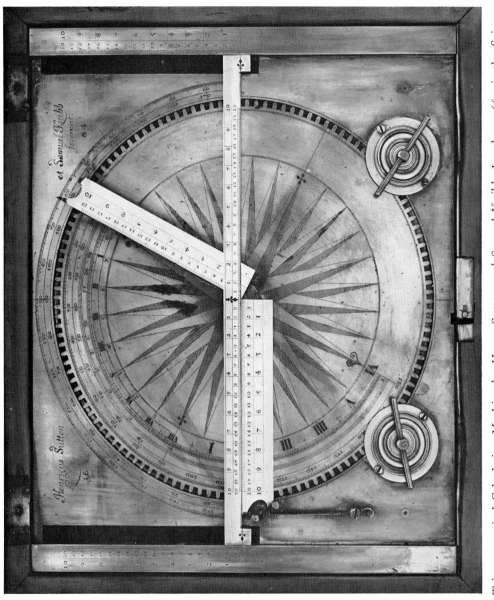

Trigonometrical Calculating Machine by Henry Sutton and Samuel Knibb, London, 1664, in the Science Museum, London.

See page 31

PLATE VII

Trigonometrical Calculating Machine by John Marke, London, 1670, in the Museum of the History of Science, Florence.

See page 31

PLATE VIII

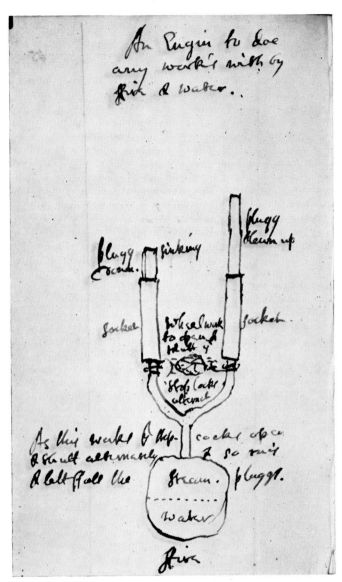

Sketch of Steam Engine, from Roger North's
Notebook, c. 1701.

See page 77

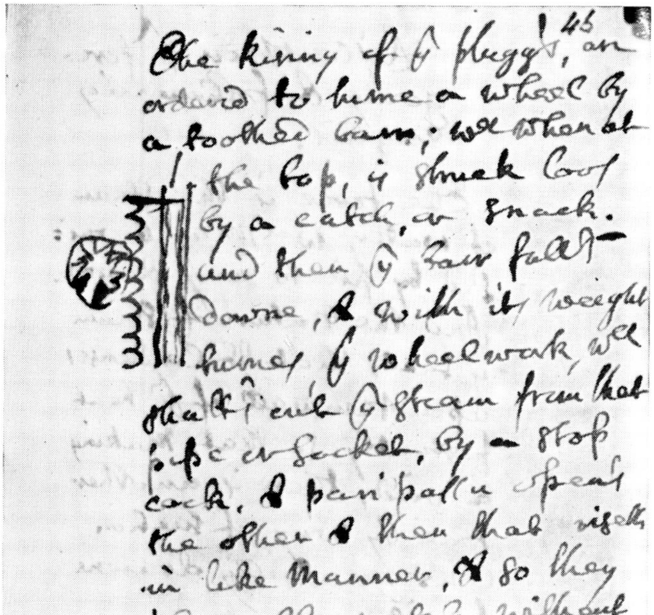

PLATE IX

Description of Steam Engine, from Roger North's
Notebook, *c.* 1701.

See page 77

PLATE X

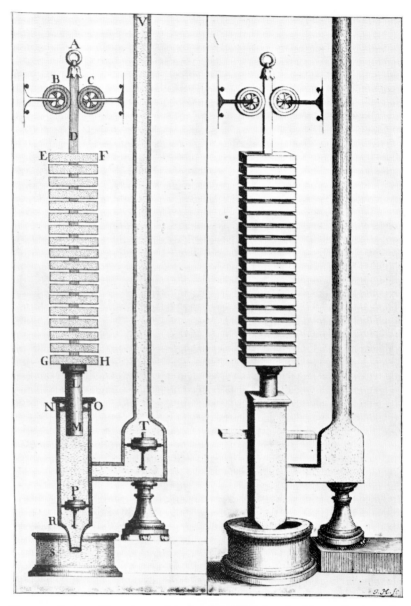

Plunger Pump. Plate from Morland's *Élévation des Eaux*, Paris, 1685.
See page 86

PLATE XI

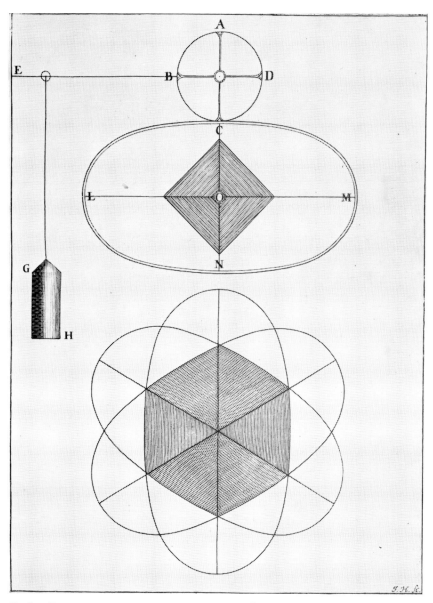

Cyclo-elliptical Motion, from Morland's *Élévation des Eaux*, Paris, 1685.
See page 86

PLATE XII

From the Miniature of Samuel Morland by Samuel
Cooper in the Victoria and Albert Museum, London.